ELIMINATION REACTIONS

REACTION MECHANISMS IN ORGANIC CHEMISTRY

A SERIES OF MONOGRAPHS EDITED BY.

E. D. HUGHES F.R.S.

Professor of Chemistry
University College
London

VOLUME 2

ELSEVIER PUBLISHING COMPANY

AMSTERDAM / LONDON / NEW YORK

ELIMINATION REACTIONS

BY

D.V. BANTHORPE PH.D.

Lecturer in Chemistry
University College
London

ELSEVIER PUBLISHING COMPANY

AMSTERDAM / LONDON / NEW YORK

1963

SOLE DISTRIBUTORS FOR THE UNITED STATES AND CANADA
AMERICAN ELSEVIER PUBLISHING COMPANY, INC.
52 VANDERBILT AVENUE, NEW YORK 17, N.Y.

SOLE DISTRIBUTORS FOR GREAT BRITAIN
ELSEVIER PUBLISHING COMPANY LIMITED
12B, RIPPLESIDE COMMERCIAL ESTATE
RIPPLE ROAD, BARKING, ESSEX

LIBRARY OF CONGRESS CATALOG CARD NUMBER 63-9912

WITH 18 TABLES

PREFACE

One of the problems associated with writing this book has been to decide what to leave out: for taken in its widest sense elimination encompasses many reactions best classified as rearrangements, and has similarities to tautomerism. My plan has been to concentrate on the familiar olefin-forming eliminations and only to mention briefly other types such as carbonyl- and nitrile-forming reactions. Even with this restricted scope, however, space has not permitted the adequate discussion of topics such as the reverse Diels-Alder and Michael reactions and homolytic eliminations. As regards the original literature, I have sometimes ignored questions of priority and completeness, especially for minor topics, and have cited a recent paper or review which contains discussion of earlier work and leading references. I think that this approach is justified, for anyone sufficiently interested to pursue the subject will soon discover the relative importance of the contributions that have been made.

It is a pleasure to acknowledge the help of several colleagues and friends who have made detailed criticisms and suggestions. Professor Sir Christopher Ingold, F.R.S., Professor E. D. Hughes, F.R.S., and Dr. C. A. Bunton have read the whole of the manuscript; and Dr. A. Maccoll, Dr. A. J. Parker, and Dr. D. Whittaker have read selected chapters. To all of them I extend my thanks.

D. V. B.

London, April 1962.

CONTENTS

Chapter 1

THE FUNDAMENTAL
MECHANISMS OF ELIMINATION

The vast collection of information concerning the interconversions of organic compounds can be classified into a small number of elementary reaction-types. One such type is elimination, which in its usually accepted sense embraces all reactions whereby a molecule decomposes by splitting off two fragments which are not replaced by other atoms or groups. This definition includes simple or complex reactions in which elimination is the overall result, and can also apply to single steps of complex reactions that may be more conveniently grouped under other classes: it extends over both homolytic and heterolytic processes, but as the latter are by far the more important and better studied, they will be considered almost exclusively in this review.

The most common elimination process, in which the two fragments are lost from adjacent atoms, is called 1,2- or β-elimination, and may be represented by reaction (1):

$$a\text{—}X\text{—}Y\text{—}b \longrightarrow \overset{+}{a} + X{=}Y + \bar{b} \tag{1}$$

X and Y must be capable of forming multiple bonds, and are usually carbon, nitrogen, or oxygen; a is almost always hydrogen. Some examples which illustrate the possible charge types are reactions (2)–(7).

$$CH_3CH_2Br \xrightarrow{\bar{O}H} \overset{+}{H} + CH_2{:}CH_2 + \bar{B}r \tag{2}$$

$$CH_3CH_2\overset{+}{N}Me_3 \xrightarrow{\bar{O}H} \overset{+}{H} + CH_2{:}CH_2 + NMe_3 \tag{3}$$

$$BrCH_2CH_2Br \xrightarrow{\bar{I}} \overset{+}{B}r + CH_2{:}CH_2 + \bar{B}r \tag{4}$$

$$CO\bar{O}CHBrCHBrPh \xrightarrow{\Delta} CO_2 + CHBr:CHPh + \bar{B}r \qquad (5)$$

$$CH_3CH_2ONO_2 \xrightarrow{\bar{O}H} \overset{+}{H} + CH_3CHO + \bar{N}O_2 \qquad (6)$$

$$CH_3CH:NOAc \xrightarrow{\bar{O}H} \overset{+}{H} + CH_3C \equiv N + \bar{O}Ac \qquad (7)$$

Other kinds of elimination are much less important. 1,4- or δ-elimination can give a stable molecule in certain structures where bond migration enables atomic octets to be preserved, eqn. (8); but 1,1- or α-elimination can only yield intermediates that are stabilised by rearrangement, eqn. (9), dimerisation, eqn. (10), or further decomposition, eqn. (11); and 1,3- or γ-elimination and higher order varieties usually form cyclic products, eqn. (12), although the former type can also result from Wagner-Meerwein rearrangement of a carbonium-ion intermediate, *cf.* eqn. (13).

$$CH_3CH:CHCH_2Br \xrightarrow{\bar{O}H} \overset{+}{H} + CH_2:CHCH:CH_2 + \bar{B}r \qquad (8)$$

$$Ph_2C:CHBr \xrightarrow{\bar{N}H_2} Ph_2C=C: \longrightarrow PhC \equiv CPh \qquad (9)$$

$$NO_2 \!-\!\!\left\langle \right\rangle\!-\!CH_2Cl \xrightarrow{\bar{O}H} NO_2\!\left\langle \right\rangle\!CH: \longrightarrow NO_2\!\left\langle \right\rangle\!CH=CH\!\left\langle \right\rangle\!NO_2 \quad (10)$$

$$CHCl_3 \xrightarrow{\bar{O}H} :CCl_2 \xrightarrow{H_2O} CO + HCOOH + \bar{C}l + \overset{+}{H} \qquad (11)$$

$$BrCH_2CH_2CH(COOEt)_2 \xrightarrow{\bar{O}H} \overset{+}{H} + CH\!\!-\!\!\!\!\underset{CH_2}{\diagdown}\!\!\!\!-\!\!C(COOEt)_2 + \bar{B}r \quad (12)$$

$$(CH_3)_3CCH_2Br \rightarrow (CH_3)_3C\overset{+}{C}H_2 \rightarrow (CH_3)_2\overset{+}{C}CH_2CH_3 \rightarrow \underset{\underset{CH_3}{|}}{CH_2:CCH_2CH_3} \quad (13)$$

Examples (10)–(12) would not be considered as eliminations on the broad definition with respect to overall chemical change, but are usually included because the initial steps are of this type.

The best known of the β-eliminations are those forming olefins, as exemplified by eqns. (2)–(5). This particular group has been extensively investigated because of its importance in preparative and structural studies and because of the ease with which the kinetics can be followed, and in all the important cases the details of the mechanisms are rather well understood [1]. Accordingly, the main discussion in subsequent chapters will centre on this type, and other varieties, about which there are little systematic data, will only be occasionally considered.

1. Basic Mechanisms for Olefin Formation

There are two levels of mechanistic interpretation: (i), the basic details concerning the number of molecules involved in the transition states of the various reaction steps; and (ii), the timing of bond breaking and more subtle points such as the stereochemistry. The obvious basic mechanisms involve either the C_β–H or the C_α–X bond breaking first or both breaking together, all with or without the influence of another reagent. Two such important mechanisms for heterolytic solution processes were discovered in the early studies. More recently a third has been recognised for gas-phase reactions, in which the homolytic-heterolytic qualification is somewhat uncertain, and there are a number of less usual types.

(a) The E2 mechanism

In 1927, Ingold initiated the mechanistic study of eliminations [2]. He noted that a strong base was almost always required to promote these reactions and he put forward a mechanism for the decomposition of quaternary ammonium salts which was later extended to other types of substrate. This, the bimolecular mechanism, is the most widespread of all elimination processes and is formulated:

$$B \overset{\frown}{\ } H\overset{\frown}{-}CR_2\overset{\downarrow}{-}CR_2\overset{\frown}{-}X \longrightarrow \overset{+}{B}H + CR_2:CR_2 + \bar{X} \qquad (14)$$

and given the symbol E2 (E, elimination; 2, bimolecular). The reagent B is basic and removes a proton from the β-carbon atom

of the substrate; the electron-attracting group X synchronously*
splits off, and the electrons transfer as shown by the curved arrows
in order to maintain the atomic octets. The reaction is second
order: first order in each component.

This mechanism occurs for X: $\cdot \overset{+}{N}R_3$, $\cdot \overset{+}{P}R_3$, $\cdot \overset{+}{S}R_2$, $\cdot \overset{+}{O}HR$, $\cdot SO_2R$,
$\cdot OSO_2R$, $\cdot OCOR$, $\cdot OOH$, $\cdot OOR$, $\cdot F$, $\cdot Cl$, $\cdot Br$, $\cdot I$, and $\cdot CN$, and
with B: H_2O, $\overline{N}R_3$, $\overline{O}H$, $\overline{O}Ac$, $\overline{O}Alk$, $\overline{O}Ar$, $\overline{N}H_2$, $\overset{=}{CO_3}$, $LiAlH_4$, $\overline{I}$,
$\overline{CN}$ and organic bases. Only a few combinations of X with B have
been studied, and in still fewer cases (*e.g.*, $\cdot \overset{+}{N}Me_3$, $\cdot \overset{+}{S}Me_2$ and
$\cdot Hal$ with $\overline{O}Et$) have the reactions been shown kinetically to be
one step and bimolecular [3]. Usually the necessity for the base
has been considered a sufficient criterion, but a large amount of
supplementary information concerning the effects of change of
structure and reaction conditions on the rate (see Chapters 2 and 3)
exists in support of the E2 concept.

Direct evidence for C_β–H breakage in the rate-determining step
has been obtained from the kinetic effects of β-deuterium substitution and some results are shown in Table 1, (sect. 3b). α-Deuter-
ation does not significantly alter the E2 rate**, but compounds
which contain β-deuterium react from 3 to 8 times more slowly
than their isotopically normal counterparts. Such isotope effects
are consistent with a synchronous mechanism, for it is well established that a C–D bond is more difficult to break than a C–H
bond [6], and according to recent views the actual magnitude
reflects the structure of the transition state [7]. In a few cases
tracer studies have also indicated the participation of C–X in the
slow step [8, 9]: the more detailed timing of the bond breakages
will be considered later (sect. 3).

The E2 mechanism cannot usually be completely isolated, for
under the conditions for its occurrence the base will act as
a nucleophile towards the α-carbon(s) and S_N2 reactions (S,

---

* A synchronous or concerted mechanism involves no intermediates and so possesses only one
transition state between the reactants and products.
** A change of rate of at most 17 % has recently been observed for α'-deuteration [4, 460]. No such
effect had been found in other systems [5].

substitution; N, nucleophilic; 2, bimolecular) will result, eqn. (15).

$$B \overset{\frown}{} R{-}X \longrightarrow B{-}\overset{+}{R} + \bar{X} \tag{15}$$

In certain structures only a small fraction may follow an E2 course, *e.g.* eqn. (16):

$$CH_3CH_2Br \xrightarrow[55°]{\overline{O}Et,\ EtOH} CH_2{:}CH_2\ (1\%) + CH_3CH_2OEt\ (99\%) \tag{16}$$

but if the total reaction is second order, a determination of the total reaction rate and a product analysis enables the rate of the E2 component to be obtained.

(b) The E1cB mechanism

Another mechanism that is consistent with second-order kinetics is eqn. (17)—a two-step process—in which proton abstraction is

$$B + CHR_2CR_2X \underset{-1}{\overset{1}{\rightleftharpoons}} \overset{+}{B}H + \bar{C}R_2CR_2X$$

$$\overset{\frown}{CR_2CR_2X} \xrightarrow{2} CR_2{:}CR_2 + \bar{X} \tag{17}$$

followed by a unimolecular ejection of $\bar{X}$ from the conjugate base of the substrate: hence the designation E1cB [10]*. A second-order rate law**, eqn. (18) is obeyed in which the rate constant depends on the relative values of k_1, k_{-1}, and k_2:

$$\text{Rate} = f(k_1,\ k_{-1},\ k_2)\ [B]\ [S] \tag{18}$$

This mechanism, which together with its variants is discussed in Chapter 4, may occur under special conditions; but for simple structures and in typical preparative procedures the E2 concerted process seems almost universal.

(c) The E1 mechanism

In 1935, Hughes [11] discovered a mechanism in which the slow

---

* Strictly, this description should only be applied when $k_{-1} > k_2$ and the first step is at equilibrium. However, we shall adopt the general practice of using E1cB as a generic term for all 2-stage mechanisms of this kind, irrespective of the rate-determining step; although EcB would be a happier choice.

** In this and subsequent discussions, B = base, S = substrate, and the brackets as shown refer to concentrations.

step is the ionisation of the substrate followed by rapid decomposition of the so-formed carbonium ion: added base is not required. This unimolecular mechanism is called E1 and is represented by eqn. (19):

$$CHR_2CR_2X \; \underset{-1}{\overset{1}{\rightleftharpoons}} \; CHR_2\overset{+}{C}R_2 + \bar{X}$$

$$CHR_2\overset{+}{C}R_2 \begin{cases} \xrightarrow{\quad 2 \quad} \overset{+}{H} + CR_2:CR_2 \\ -Y: \xrightarrow{\quad 3 \quad} CHR_2CR_2\overset{+}{Y} \end{cases} \qquad (19)$$

The carbonium ion is partitioned between elimination and substitution; the latter being the result of neutralisation by a solvent molecule Y, or any available nucleophile.

The rate law is more complex than for E2: on application of the steady state approximation to the concentration of the carbonium ion (which should be reactive enough to justify this procedure, for k_{-1}, k_2 and k_3 are extremely large), an expression (20) is obtained,

$$\text{Rate of elimination} = \frac{k_1 k_2 \, [S]}{k_2 + k_3 \, [Y] + k_{-1} \, [\bar{X}]} \qquad (20)$$

and if

$$k' = [k_2 + k_3 \, [Y]], \text{ and is } > k_{-1} \, [\bar{X}]$$

then

$$\text{Rate of elimination} = \frac{k_1 k_2 [S]}{k'} \qquad (21)$$

The kinetics of E1 reactions are indeed usually good first-order in the substrate concentration although often a weak base such as pyridine must be added in order to prevent the acid which is formed from re-adding to the olefin and forming an equilibrium mixture. Inspection of eqn. (20) shows that a common-ion retardation effect could occur both during a run and on initial addition of $\bar{X}$, but such an effect has never been illustrated for an E1 reaction in those hydroxylic solvents in which salt effects can be easily interpreted— partly because elimination is only a minor component in such conditions and partly because carbonium ions are very labile in

these media and so k_2 and k_3 are large—and the inequality leading
to eqn. (21) holds. Thus the measured rate constant, k_1k_2/k' is
equal to the rate constant for ionisation multiplied by the fraction
of the reaction which leads to olefin. Common-ion effects do occur
in aprotic, non-solvolytic media but here there are additional
difficulties of interpretation due to long-range effects, ionic aggrega-
tion, intermediate mechanisms, etc.

The E1 mechanism occurs for X; $\cdot\overset{+}{S}Me_2$, $\cdot\overset{+}{N}Me_3$, $\cdot Cl$, $\cdot Br$; $\cdot\overset{+}{O}HR$,
$\cdot I$, $\cdot\overset{+}{O}H_2$, $\cdot\overset{+}{N}_2$, $\cdot OCOR$, and $\cdot OSO_2R$ but usually only in specially
chosen structures and conditions, and then often as a minor
component. For example, *tert.*-butyl compounds in 60% aqueous
ethanol at 25° (an especially favourable case, see later) give only
16% E1 with 84% S_N1, and α-phenylethyl compounds give 100%
S_N1 [12]. In only a few cases have full kinetic analyses been
carried through and usually the observation that a reaction is
unaccelerated by added base (after allowance is made for any
ionic-strength effects) is taken as sufficient to indicate that an E1
is occurring rather than an E2 involving the solvent as base. This
is very reasonable, for the lyate ions of the common solvents are
so much stronger bases than the solvent molecules that they
would easily dominate a competition for the substrate, even when
present in relatively low concentration.

E1 is favoured by a substrate structure and an environment
which aids ionisation and is thus facilitated over E2 for secondary,
tertiary, and α-arylated halides in aqueous or polar solvents, and
can best compete with S_N1 in fairly solvating but poorly-nucleophilic media such as sulphur dioxide and formic acid. Unlike the
situation in E2 reactions, rearrangements typical of carbonium-ion
processes can often occur [13].

As the olefin is formed from an ion, the yield (and also the relative
proportions of isomers, if any, can be formed) should be independent
of the leaving group X for a given alkyl structure under standard
conditions, and this is found to be approximately the case for
tert.-butyl [14a], *tert.*-pentyl [14b], *sec.*-octyl [14c], and menthyl
halides and 'onium compounds [14d] in hydroxylic solvents. Thus
for *tert.*-butyl compounds a series with a range of ionisation rates

of 900-fold gives the same olefin yield to $\pm 15\%$ (of the actual value). The carbonium ion almost certainly decomposes under these conditions while the counter-ion is still very near—perhaps even in physical contact as an ion-pair—and so it is not surprising that a small dependence on the nature of X is obtained. In less reactive media of high dielectric constant, such as nitromethane or acetonitrile, the ions should be more independent and these small differences might disappear.

Proton loss from a carbonium ion is fast, but it does require activation. This is shown by the different temperature coefficients of the products of E1 and S_N1 reactions [1], and it can be calculated from these that the former process has an activation energy in excess of the other by about 2–4.5 kcal.mole^{-1}. As the destruction of a carbonium ion by the solvent in an S_N1 reaction is probably unactivated [15], the absolute values of the activation energies of elimination will lie in this range.

These low activation energies are reflected in the low β-deuterium isotope effects* for the olefin-forming steps and also the low isotope effects for the reverse processes [16]—the protonations of olefins (sect. 3b, Table 1 and discussion). It is interesting that an isotope effect of a similar size is obtained for the initial ionisation although no β-hydrogen bond is broken in this step [17, 18], and this has been attributed to the smaller hyperconjugative stabilisation of the incipient ion by a C_β–D bond than by a C_β–H** [17, 19], and also to steric effects [20].

The details of the proton loss, which usually occurs to a solvent molecule, are not clear. In hydroxylic solvents, the slightly acidic β-hydrogens of a carbonium ion could hydrogen-bond to a particular solvent molecule (which in turn is part of a hydrogen-bonded solvent structure) and ultimately be transferred to the same. It has been suggested [17] that such bonding appears during the ionisation step and that "elimination-type driving forces" assist

---

* Isotopic substitution can affect both the activation energy and the pre-exponential factor, but the change in the former is usually the major influence.

** There seems no necessity to introduce the concept of hydrogen participation via a bridged-structure between the α- and β-carbon atoms [21] in this or any other contexts to be discussed.

this step and account for the isotope effects. An alternative view is that the proton is abstracted by a solvent molecule that has broken substantially free of the ordered structure of the liquid and penetrates the solvation shell around the ion. The ensuing proton transfer could occur on every encounter, but such events would be controlled by the rate of diffusion of the reactants through the quasi-crystalline solvent lattice: these processes are known to show an "apparent" activation energy of about 4 kcal.-mole^{-1} on account of the variation of the viscosity of the solvent with temperature. A similar explanation could apply to the S_N1 union of a carbonium ion and an anion, which requires an activation of 4 kcal.mole^{-1*} that has been attributed to the necessity for an energy of desolvation before the ions can enter the transition state [15]. The unactivated decomposition of a carbonium ion by the solvent, however, probably proceeds by a collapse of the solvation shell about the α-carbon atom.

In aprotic media the transfer occurs to a basic solute, either added or formed during the reaction (e.g. Cl$^-$ or HCl$_2$$^-$) and here the kinetics indicate that the base concentration does not enter into the rate expression: the base merely being a passive proton acceptor the presence of which prevents immediate back-addition to the nascent olefin. There also appears to be no evidence for an E2C mechanism, eqn. (22) in these solvents—analogous to the

$$HCR_2CR_2X \underset{-1}{\overset{1}{\rightleftharpoons}} HCR_2\overset{+}{C}R_2 + \bar{X}$$

(22)

$$B + HCR_2\overset{+}{C}R_2 \overset{2}{\longrightarrow} \overset{+}{B}H + CR_2{:}CR_2$$

known S_N2C process [22]—in which step 2 is rate-determining.

It would be interesting to know the energetics of processes in aprotic media, for the availability of the solute at the reaction centre would now be controlled by electrostatics rather than by diffusion, and solvation shells would not be so important.

Base-promoted E2 reactions in hydroxylic solvents are invariably

---

* On the assumption that the S_N1 involving the solvent has zero activation-energy.

irreversible, but E1 reactions are reversible, at least in principle, and so, information concerning their mechanism may be obtained by studying the reverse reaction, for the principle of microscopic reversibility requires that a reversible process must proceed through the same intermediates in the forward and reverse directions, although in opposite sequence. This approach has not been applied to the E1 reactions of halides etc. in hydroxylic solvents, because the reverse reaction—the addition of hydrogen halides to olefins—is complicated by solvent intervention, but it has been used for such additions in aprotic media and can define the number and types of molecules constituting the transition states of these processes. Some other applications are discussed in Chapter 6, sect. 4a.

(d) Intermediate mechanisms

In their early papers on S_N and E reactions, Hughes and Ingold suggested that there could be a continuous range of mechanisms between the uni- and bimolecular extremes [10], and although this idea has attracted little attention in the E case, a lively (but rather hazy) controversy has resulted in the other field [23]. The point in dispute is whether, under certain "borderline conditions", concurrent (or mixed) mechanisms of uni- and bi-molecular processes occur which obey a rate law, eqn. (23), and show the stereochemical consequences and dependence of rate on medium and structure as expected from such a duality, or an intermediate mechanism exists which defies description in terms of these concepts or interpretation by the usual criteria for molecularity, and obeys a rate law, eqn. (24) in which $f[B]$ is some function of the base concentration.

$$\text{Rate} = k_1 [S] + k_2 [S] [B] \tag{23}$$

$$\text{Rate} = k [S] f [B] \tag{24}$$

Borderline reactions in hydroxylic solvents, such as the decomposition of iso-propyl bromide [24] and menthyl 'onium compounds [14d] in alkaline aqueous ethanol, can be analysed satisfactorily in terms of concurrent E1, E2, S_N1, and S_N2 processes, and we shall confine our discussion to these models and attribute various differences between reactions to variations in the structure of the E1 or E2 transition states. A brief discussion of the semantic difficulties involved, in rigid definitions and the limits to which mechanisms can be delineated, has been given by Bunton [25].

2. The Stereochemistry of Elimination

The early literature [26] contains many indications that *trans*-elimination cf. (I, II) is the mode for base-promoted eliminations, and in 1940 Hückel realised that the stereochemistry should be dependent on the mechanism [27]. Hughes and Ingold subsequently developed [3] a theory for E1 and E2, based on the stereochemical rules known to apply to substitution, which provided the background to the experimental work later to be performed.

(a) E2 reactions

The stereo-requirement for E2 in the system $H–C_\beta–C_\alpha–X$ is that the electrons from the $C_\beta–H$ bond should enter the octet of C_α on the opposite side to the leaving $C_\alpha–X$ electrons. This minimises the repulsion energy between the electron-pairs (in a manner analogous to that occurring in the Walden Inversion) and results in a trans-planar conformation for the substrate in the transition state, as is shown in Newman projection (I). *cis*-Elimination, if it occurred,

trans-Elimination   cis-Elimination
(I)   (II)

might be expected, for steric reasons, from a staggered conformation similar to (II) rather than from a completely eclipsed structure. On the basis of a recent system of nomenclature [28], (I) and (II), and the eclipsed structure are classified as *anti*-periplanar, *syn*-clinal, and *syn*-periplanar conformations respectively.

Hückel's pioneer work involved cyclic systems with restricted rotation about C–C bonds, in which a rigid orientation of the leaving groups could be maintained; and he found that elimination only proceeded when trans-planar arrangements could be achieved (see Chap. 5, sect. 3). The same requirement has been demonstrated in acyclic structures under E2 kinetically-controlled conditions by means of the isomers (III) and (IV), each of which only gave the olefin resulting from *trans*-elimination, eqns. (26) *[29]*; and exactly

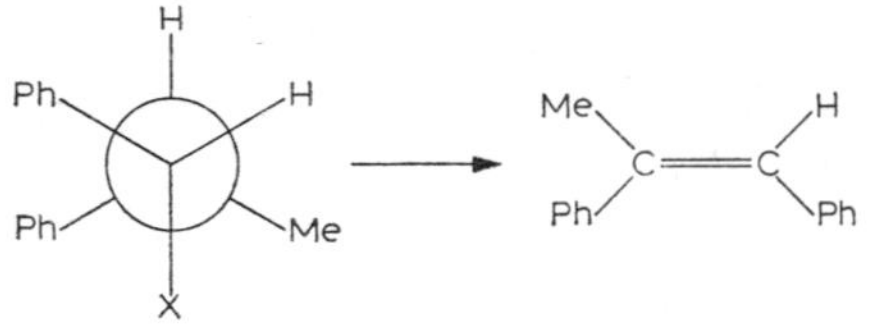

(III)

(26)

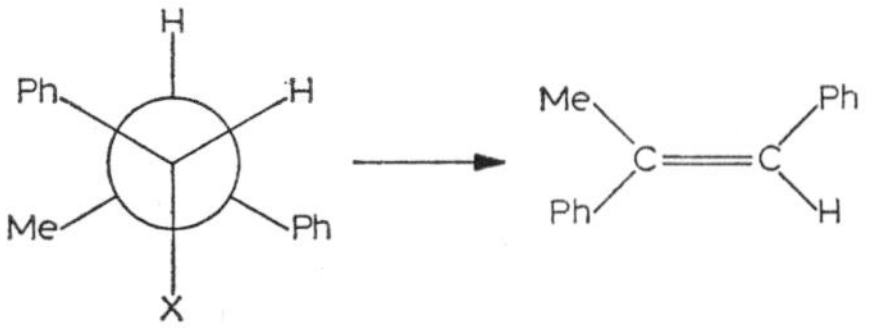

(IV)

$$(X = Cl, Br, \overset{+}{N}Me_3)$$

similar is the earlier demonstration of complete *trans*-stereo-specificity for the debromination of the isomeric 2,3-dibromo-butanes by iodide ion *[30]*. The importance of the *trans*-orientation of the leaving groups is shown by the observation that E2 dehydro-halogenation of β-benzenehexachloride (V), in which all the chlorine atoms are *trans*, proceeded with an activation energy some 12 kcal.-mole^{-1} greater than that for the reactions of the other isomers, all of which have at least one pair of chlorine and hydrogen situated *trans [31, 32]*. In certain other ring systems (VI), where the leaving groups cannot attain planarity but which do not possess the rigidity of the last example, a failure to attain the most favoured geometry by an angle $\vartheta \sim 60°$ (VII) increased the activation energy by 5–8 kcal.mole⁻¹ above that for the unrestricted benzene hexa-chlorides [33]; and for acyclic systems where a bulky β-linked R caused $\vartheta \sim 30°$, an energy increase of ca. 2.0 kcal.mole⁻¹ was obtained above that of unrestricted homologues [34].

(V)   (VI)   (VII)

Hückel's explanation for *trans*-specificity was that a negatively charged or dipolar base would be repelled by the exposed negative end of the dipole $\overset{\delta+\ \ \delta-}{C-X}$ on the leaving group, and so would be directed into the *trans*-position with respect to it. Calculations show that such an influence is quite inadequate to account for the large energy differences that are involved [31b], and this theory was disproved by the observation that compounds with charged leaving groups, e.g., ·NMe₃, underwent *trans*-elimination, although, in this case, electrostatic forces would have favoured a *cis*-process. Such *trans*-eliminations have been proved in a few cases by product analyses of decompositions yielding geometrical isomers, and recent extensive kinetic studies on simple aliphatic ammonium and sulphonium compounds are best interpreted on this stereo-chemistry [34].

(b) E1 reactions

The situation is now more complex, but was considered by Hughes and Ingold [3] as being governed by carbonium-ion stability. It is convenient to regard ionisation as a series of equilibria (25) in-

$$RX \rightleftharpoons \overset{+}{R}\overset{-}{X} \rightleftharpoons \overset{+}{R} \text{ (solv.) } \overset{-}{X} \rightleftharpoons \overset{+}{R} \text{ (solv.) } + \overset{-}{X} \text{ (solv.)} \qquad (25)$$

(VIII)   (IX)   (X)

volving differing degrees of solvation and independence of the ions, and kinetic evidence for such a scheme has been obtained for certain acetolyses *[35]*.

The initially formed ion-pair consists of ions in close contact; and the configuration at the α-carbon would be retained insomuch as very reactive ions, which would decompose through this species, would show *trans*-elimination for the same reason as in the E2 case. Elimination could occur only if a suitably placed β-hydrogen was available (XI), but such an ionising conformation would usually be achieved, for C–X fission would be largely assisted by hyperconjugation, when the axis of the *p*-orbital being developed was co-planar with a C_β–H bond. Substitution would predominate for ionising conformations, such as (XII). A less reactive species (VIII) could undergo (and a less reactive solvent would permit) conversion to (IX) (solvated, but not independent ions) or (X) (free ions), and both of these species would be planar at the α-carbon atom and

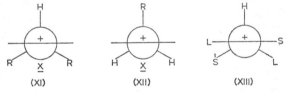

(XI)   (XII)   (XIII)

In (XI) and (XII) complete planarity   L and S are larger and
at the α-carbon is probably not achieved   smaller substituents

could rotate into a conformation (XIII), such that bulky groups did not come *cis* in the resulting olefin, and a mixture of overall *cis*- and *trans*-elimination would result.

There are not many data available with which to check these deductions. In hydroxylic solvents species (IX) and (X) usually seem to be achieved, and several examples will be given later. Nevertheless, the dehydrations of certain cyclohexanols (which almost certainly proceed via E1) show discrimination in favour of *trans*-elimination *[36–38]*.

E2 reactions involve one stage, but in certain cases E1 can be multi-stage aside from such niceties as solvation equilibria: thus any number of fast steps can occur after the slow ionisation, which cannot be elucidated by kinetic means but only by product studies on suitably constructed compounds. Cram has analysed such a situation for the solvolysis of (XIV) in acetic acid [39], where the various solvation steps should be distinct on account of the good ionising, but poor dissociating and nucleophilic properties of the medium. Classical and non-classical carbonium ions, rearrangement, and neighbouring group participation are evoked and a simplified scheme [27] is appended.

(OTs = tosylate; A: *trans*-stereospecific elimination product,
B: non-stereospecific elimination product.)

(XV) is an intimate ion-pair, and (XVI) a non-classical bridged ion, the presence of which, as an intermediate, is not, however, essential to the analysis. The former leads to *trans* elimination, as does the latter, which can only be formed from the conformation of (XIV) shown. Such a profusion of pathways is unlikely for the usual alkyl structures in more polar solvents and would be much more difficult to detect (*e.g.* by tracer studies) in systems not possessing the potentialities of the above for optical and structural isomerism.

3. The Structure of the Transition State

The necessity for a trans-planar E2 conformation does not define the geometry of all the bonds in the transition state, for it is not a requirement of any concerted mechanism that all the bond changes should keep exactly in pace with one another, and as, in this case, these changes are spread over five atoms, it is easy for one or more to move ahead of the others before this state is reached [8, 29, 34].

Three types of transition state, A, B, and C, can be visualised for E2 according to the bond changes which make the more progress initially, but all represent reactions which are still concerted in

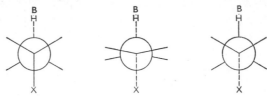

(A) E1cB-like   (B) Fully synchronous E2   (C) E1-like

the sense that one bond fission could not proceed without the others, as is shown by the lack of β-deuterium exchange with the solvent and by the observed second-order kinetics. Types A and C are similar in configuration to the initial reactants (*cf.* the previous discussion of retention of configuration on ionisation) and B resembles the final products in having the flattest structure and the best developed double-bond. In an analogous manner two models can be considered for each of the ionisation and product steps of E1, being similar either to the reactants or products.

The molecular events of a particular reaction may belong to a range of transition state types, but one of these will predominate in the Boltzmann distribution and it must approximate to one of the chosen models. This favoured structure will be considered as *the* transition state of the reaction and its nature will be controlled by structure and environment in a predictable manner. In this section we will consider four experimental approaches: through energy relationships, isotope effects, kinetics, and analyses of products; by which deductions may be made concerning these structures, and then using these indications we will predict what structures will occur for particular reactions.

(a) Energy relationships

The major part of the energy of any reacting system is electronic, and depends on the distances of the electrons from their nuclei (distances which, for states of like charge, can be roughly correlated with the unsaturation present). Consequently, Catchpole, Hughes and Ingold suggested [40] that the distribution of electrons in a transition state would resemble either that in the reactants or the products, according to which lay higher on the free-energy curve. This idea is best illustrated by means of the free-energy diagram (XVII) representing an endo-energetic reaction. If the curve does not possess disproportionate slopes on each side of the maximum, it can be seen that the transition state is similar in energy, and hence also in electronic structure, to the products and that the smaller the ratio of the free energy of activation $\Delta G^{\ddagger}$ is, to the total free-energy change $\Delta G°$, the closer will be this resemblance.

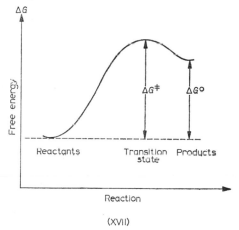

(XVII)

In an analogous manner, an exo-energetic reaction will possess a structure similar to the reactants.

Other workers, especially Hammond [11], have considered a correlation between free-energy change and molecular geometry, but there is no principle that the configuration of the atoms in a reacting molecule should change in phase with the energy, and it is not always safe to deduce that, for example, the transition state of an exo-energetic reaction should resemble initial reactants in geometrical structure.

As applied to elimination, however, certain deductions can be made by means of this approach. Typical E2 reactions of alkyl halides and 'onium compounds are shown by approximate thermo-chemical calculations and by their complete irreversibility to be exo-energetic and so should possess electronic configurations resembling those of the reactants. This makes transition states of types A or C seem likely. The formation of a carbonium ion occurs further along the reaction coordinate, for it is endo-energetic and highly reversible, but the olefin forming step in E1 is a high-energy releasing process of low activation energy, and so involves a transition state very similar in electronic structure to a carbonium ion.

(b) Isotope effects

These conclusions are supplemented by some β-deuterium isotope effects for E2 reactions, which are listed in Table 1. Some of these effects are smaller than expected from theoretical considerations, and this has been attributed to a smaller degree of bond-breaking in the transition state. This idea can be criticised as being inconsistent with absolute rate theory, on the basis of which the theoretical values are calculated, and which requires the C_β–H vibration to pass completely over to translation in the transition state, with no intermediate degrees of breakage. A more sophisticated treatment [7] shows that the low isotope effects will occur, when the critical configuration of C_β ... H ... B resembles either that in the reactants or the products (28), and that for intermediate cases the full theoretical maximum will be shown.

$$
\begin{array}{lll}
\text{C .. H .... B} & \text{(type C)} & \text{Low isotope effect} \\
\text{C .... H .. B} & \text{(type A, B)} & \text{Low isotope effect} \qquad (28) \\
\text{C ... H ... B} & \text{(type A, B)} & \text{Large isotope effect}
\end{array}
$$

On this basis, examples 1–3 (Table 1) have undergone intermediate proton transfer in the transition state, which must thus correspond to types A or B, and the β-phenylethyl compounds differ in the order $7 > 6 > 4$ towards either of the extremes A or C, for a low isotope effect either indicates extensive proton transfer or very

TABLE 1

SOME β-DEUTERIUM ISOTOPE EFFECTS IN ELIMINATION

E2	System	Temp.* (°C)	$\frac{k_H}{k_D}$ obs.**	$\frac{k_H}{k_D}$ calc.**	Ref.
1	$CD_3CH_2\overset{+}{N}Me_3$ + $\overline{O}H$	137	4.0	4.0	43a
2	$(CD_3)_2CHBr$ + $\overline{O}Et$	25	6.7	6.9	5
3	$PhCDCH_3CH_2Br$ + $\overline{O}Et$	25	7.5	6.9	43a
4	$PhCD_2CH_2Br$ + $\overline{O}Et$	30	7.1	6.6	44
5	$PhCD_2CH_2Br$ + $\overline{O}Bu^t$	30	7.9	6.6	44
6	$PhCD_2CH_2\overset{+}{S}Me_2$ + $\overline{O}Et$	30	5.1	6.6	44
7	$PhCD_2CH_2\overset{+}{N}Me_3$ + $\overline{O}Et$	50	3.0	6.0	44

* These effects are temperature dependent.
** Relative rates of normal and deuterated species.

E1	System	Solvent	$\frac{k_H}{k_D}$ ion.*	$\frac{k_H}{k_D}$ prod.*	Ref.
8	$(CH_3)_2CDC(CH_3)_2Br$	EtOH–H_2O	1.3	1.3	17b
9	$CH_3CD_2C(CD_3)_2Br$	EtOH–H_2O	2.3	1.7	17a
10	$CH_3CH_2CD_2CHBrCD_3$	HCOOH	1.7	—	18
11	$CH_3CH_2CD_2CH(OSOCl)CD_3$	dioxan	1.4	1.0	18
12	$CH_3CH_2CD_2CH(OSOCl)CD_3$	pentane	3.3	1.0	18

* Isotope effects on ionisation and product forming steps.

little [42]. Later we shall see that it is reasonable to expect 'onium compounds to transfer a proton to base more completely than the bromide would, and so the former would be type A and the latter type B. What this criterion does not reveal is the degree of fission in bonds other than C_β–H, thus a small isotope effect is consistent with types A, B, or C and a large effect with A or B. Saunders has shown [8] that the C_α S isotope effect for compound 6, (Table 1), was only 10% of the theoretical maximum, and recently a slightly larger C_α–N effect was found [9] for example, 7, and both these results (in conjunction with the C_β–effects) are best interpreted as indicating a predominantly type A (E1cB-like) transition state: the more so, surprisingly, for the sulphonium compound. This isotope data is also consistent with an E1cB scheme, which seems likely for such structures and reaction conditions (see Chap. 4, sect. 1), but the lack of β-deuterium exchange over a wide range of basicities rules out the mechanism [44, 60].

Example 5, (Table 1), exhibits an isotope effect that is considerably larger than theory would predict, and although it is dangerous to speculate too deeply about non-agreement with a simplified theory which, for instance, completely neglects the contribution of C_β–H bending vibrations to the energy and also the effect on the entropy of activation, it has been suggested [43b] that this high value is due to non-classical proton-transfer by the tunnel-effect. Other evidence for this effect has recently been presented [45], and if it is a widespread occurrence a reassessment of the agreement between observed and theoretical isotope effects will be required, for the latter are calculated with no allowance for this phenomenon.

E1 reactions show small isotope effects for both ionisation and olefin-forming stages. An explanation of the former has already been given and, in agreement with this, these effects are approximately temperature-independent [18] (cf. the E2 kinetic effects). If the hyperconjugative viewpoint is maintained, a slight decrease in isotope effect with an increase of temperature is to be expected, whereas the reverse should occur if steric factors are controlling; but experiments of sufficient accuracy to permit a decision have not yet been performed. The results for the olefin-forming step are in accord with the predicted low activation energy of this step. Examples 11 and 12 show no isotope effect on the products, but although these have been interpreted as E1 it is likely that, for this leaving group and in such non-polar solvents, a one-step cyclic mechanism occurs in which there is considerable C–O stretching but little C_β–H breakage (cf. Chap. 7, sect. 5). Recently, product isotope-effects of 2.5 and 3.1 have been obtained [46] for the solvolysis and silver-ion catalysed decomposition of deuterated *tert*-pentyl chloride, and the surprisingly large latter value suggests an increase in the stability of the carbonium ion under these conditions. The much more reactive ion* from deamination of the corresponding amine showed a product isotope-effect of only 1.5.

(c) Product and kinetic analyses

By an ingenious combination of kinetic and product analyses, Cram has shown [29] that the base-strength, the nature of the leaving group, and the solvating power of the medium, can all affect the structure of the E2 transition state in a reasonable way. His method was to use the isomers (III) and (IV) (sect. 2a) which both possess unstrained initial conformations but which yield olefins, in which the two phenyl groups are *cis* and *trans* respectively. A transition state in which the two phenyls came *cis*, across a well developed double bond, would be expected to involve much more steric strain than one where the groups came *trans*, and so the elimination rate should be smaller in the former case (any observed effect should be entirely steric, for polar influences should balance in the two instances). If the transition state was of types A or C and there was little flattening of the molecule and double-bond formation, there should be little difference in the rate of elimination from (III) and (IV). In practice, the ratio of the E2 rates for these isomers varied from 1 to 57 for different leaving groups in ethanol or *tert*-butanol with the corresponding lyate ion as base. It was concluded from this that 'onium salts in ethanol reacted through transition states of type B, but changed to type A in the more basic butoxide–butanol system. Model C was favoured for halides in ethanol, for here there was a good ionising medium and a relatively weak base, but this changed to type B in *tert*.-butanol in which the stronger base favoured proton removal and the medium discouraged the ionisation of C–X, and so a more concerted process resulted.

Less detailed earlier studies showed that for dehalogenation [47], dehydrohalogenation [48], and base-catalysed ester decompositions

---

* The nature of the ionic intermediate in deamination is considered in Chap. 6, sect. 6.

[49] which formed stilbenes, the olefin with the two *trans*-phenyl groups was formed up to 130-fold faster than when the groups came *cis*.* Here the maximum difference in the free-energy of activation is about 2.8 kcal.mole^{-1}, and this compares with an energy difference between the final products of 5.7 kcal.mole^{-1}, which, if it was fully exhibited in the transition state, would lead to a rate difference of 10^4 between the isomers. Once the steric non-bonding energy had made its appearance, it would increase very rapidly with a slight flattening of the type B structure, and so it seems that double-bond character is fairly well developed in these cases. A similar instance occurs in the decomposition of 2-bromobutane, which gives the *trans*-2-olefin at a rate six times that of the *cis*-isomer *[51]*. Here the energy difference between the two butenes corresponds to a maximum change of rate of only nine-fold.

The variation in the geometry of the transition state, caused by changing the leaving group under otherwise standard conditions, is shown in Table 2. For the first seven entries the $C=C$ bond increasingly develops in the transition state, for there is an increasing tendency to favour *trans*- over *cis*-olefin formation. For the 'onium salts especially, the geometry must be very similar to the initial state (type A), for there is practically no difference in the rates of the reactions leading to *cis*- and *trans*-isomers. The last three entries show that an α- or β-linked phenyl group must so stabilise the double-bond formation that the typical 'onium-type geometry is largely lost; considerable type B character emerges; and little *cis*-olefin is formed. The Hammett σ-ϱ equation is obeyed by para-substituted β-phenylethyl compounds, and the magnitude of the reaction constant has been used to elucidate the nature of the transition state *[42]*. Such deductions obviously cannot be extrapolated to alkyl systems, and some limitations of the approach are outlined in Chap. 3, sect. 2.

E1 reactions only show appreciable steric effects when the groups which eclipse in the transition state leading to the *cis*-olefin are

---

* Much smaller rate differences (*ca.* 8-fold) have recently been found for the isomeric dichlorostil-benes *[50]*.

TABLE 2

cis-trans-OLEFIN FORMATION IN E2

Compound, X	Conditions	*trans/cis-2-ene*	Eclipsing groups	Ref.
2-Butyl·$\overset{+}{N}Me_3\overline{O}H$	Pyrolysis	0.7	Me, Me	[52]
2-Pentyl·$\overset{+}{N}Me_3$	$\overline{O}Et$, EtOH; pyrolysis	1,0, 0.8	Et, Me	[52,53]
2-Pentyl·$\overset{+}{S}Me_2$	$\overline{O}Et$, EtOH	1.6	Et, Me	[53]
2-Pentyl·OTs	$\overline{O}Et$, EtOH	1.9	Et, Me	[53]
2-Pentyl·Br	$\overline{O}Et$, EtOH	2.8	Et, Me	[53]
2-Pentyl·I	$\overline{O}Et$, EtOH	3.4	Et, Me	[53]
2-Pentyl·SO_2CH_3	$\overline{O}Et$, EtOH	3.6	Et, Me	[53]
1,2-Diphenylethyl·$\overset{|}{N}Me_3\overline{O}H$	Pyrolysis	"very large"	Ph, Ph	[54]
3-Phenylpropyl-2-$\overset{+}{N}Me_3\overline{O}H$	Pyrolysis	"very large"	Ph, Me	[55]
1-Phenylpropyl-1-$\overset{+}{N}Me_3\overline{O}H$	Pyrolysis	"very large"	Ph, Me	[56]

TABLE 3

cis-trans-OLEFIN FORMATION IN E1 *[57]*

Compound	*trans/cis-2-ene*	Eclipsing groups
Butyl-2-tosylate	1.1	Me, Me
Pentyl-2-tosylate	1.4	Me, Et
4-Methylpentyl-2-tosylate	2.0	Me, Pr[i]
4,4-Dimethylpentyl-2-tosylate	83	Me, Bu[t]

bulky. Thus for the first and last examples in Table 3 the difference in the free energy of activation between reactions leading to *cis*- and *trans*-olefin is 0.06 and 2.7 kcal.mole^{-1}, whereas if the full influence of the free energy difference between the isomers was felt, these would become 1.0 and 4.3 kcal, respectively. The appreciable fraction of this energy shown in the last case might be considered to be contrary to the conclusion, drawn from thermochemical and isotope-effect arguments, that the E1 transition state for olefin-formation should resemble the carbonium ion, but the change of hybridisation at the α-carbon, to form such an ion, could permit steric compressions between the large α- and β-substituents, to a greater degree than would occur for the simpler structures, and so steric effects might well arise in a structure very little removed from a carbonium ion.

(d) General predictions for transition state structures

The conclusions that can be drawn from Cram's quantitative studies are limited in that they apply to atypical structures containing two phenyl groups, which, as reference to Table 2 will show, may have a decisive influence not present in simple cases. The balance between the factors which do influence the geometry of the transition state is delicate but the predictions set out below seem reasonable and are in accord with the experimental evidence which has just been considered.

Type A (E1cB-like) should be favoured for compounds with β-hydrogen atoms made labile by the inductive effects of β- (phenyl, halogen) or α- (positively charged) substituents, and the rate of reactions proceeding through such a structure should be markedly affected by factors which influence the acidity of these β-hydrogens, but not greatly so by substituents possessing conjugative capabilities or potential *cis*-steric effects. The type should be favoured if strong bases are used and in solvents which do not favour the ionisation of the α-linked group. A wide range of β-isotope effects should occur, but with a tendency for small values. In general, 'onium salts in strongly basic, polar conditions (*e.g.* $\overline{O}H$ in H_2O) and alkyl halides in basic but relatively non-polar conditions (*e.g. tert.*-BuO in *tert.*-BuOH) should belong to this type.

Type C (E1-like) should be favoured by all factors, such as electron release to the α-carbon and steric and solvent effects, which favour C_α–X fission. The strength of the base and polar and steric effects of β-substituents should be relatively unimportant, but as unsaturation is developed at the α-carbon, α-substituents capable of conjugation should affect the rate. The β-deuterium effect should be small. This type of transition state should occur especially for secondary, tertiary, and α-arylated halides in dissociating solvents with bases of moderate strength*.

Type B (E2 concerted) possesses the obvious characteristics of both of the above, with susceptibility to conjugating substituents at both α- and β-positions and a high β-deuterium isotope effect. Only for this case should the bulk of the α- and β-substituents cause extensive *cis*-effects, as the double bond is now well developed. Both halides and 'onium compounds should approach this structure from opposite extremes as the appropriate variables are altered.

For E1 reactions, the main details—the degree of flattening at the α-carbon, the C–H bond stretching, and C=C formation—will be governed by the degree of solvation of the ion (sect. 2) and the factors discussed in the above cases. Specific examples of these transition states will be discussed in later chapters.

The stereo-consequences of the E2 transition states are of interest. Types B and C should be *trans*-specific, but it has been suggested [42] that type A might show a relaxation of this normal stereorequirement. In reference to the last case Ingold has considered E2 to be a combination of the S_E2 replacement of H_β at C_β by C_α as an electrophile together with the S_N2 displacement of X from C_α by C_β. By analogy with the known stereochemistry of S_E2 displacements at a saturated carbon atom, he has suggested [58] that a *cis*-orientation of the α- and β-linked leaving groups would be preferred, if the C_β–H bond were largely ionised before reaching the transition state. Data are not available with which to check this prediction.

---

* In practice it is found that the decompositions of such structures with as strong a base as ethoxide on in ethanol utilise this type of transition state [29].

Chapter 2

THE INFLUENCE OF ENVIRONMENTAL FACTORS
ON RATE AND MECHANISM

The yield of olefin from a particular substrate depends on the reaction conditions, for these influence both the mechanism and the relative importance of substitution and elimination for a particular mechanism. The structure of the substrate controls the innate tendency for reaction by a specific path, but this tendency can be overruled by the effects of the environment, a knowledge of which is thus essential in order to isolate a particular reaction of a desired molecularity. The environmental variables are the concentration and strength of the base, the solvent, the temperature, and the ionic-strength, but these are not all independent and their effects cannot be completely disentangled. An in-appreciation of the influence of these led to monumental confusion in the early elimination studies.

1. Concentration of the Base

If a compound can react by unimolecular mechanisms, these will occur at low base concentrations in a solvent favouring ionisation, and will nearly always give a low olefin yield. A bimolecular component will usually appear as the base concentration is increased and at high concentrations this may completely take control, for the ratio of the total bimolecular and total unimolecular rate is proportional to the concentration of the basic reagent. The fraction of reaction leading to elimination under these latter conditions will be independent of the base concentration for both S_N2 and E2 have the same kinetic form, but this proportion will vary with the changing base concentration in the region of mixed order: the variation being more rapid the more basic the reagent.

At very high basicities, there may not be enough solvent molecules to provide the usual complement of the solvation shell of each solute molecule* and as a result the base may enter the rate-expression for elimination through a basicity function [59] (rather than the concentration) analogous to the Hammett functions which measure the protonating ability of concentrated acid solutions.

Very recently, a good correlation of the rate of an E2 process possessing an E1cB-like transition state with a basicity function has been obtained up to $4M$ sodium methoxide in methanol: a more concerted E2 had a varying order in methoxide in this range that was greater than unity but did not correlate with the basicity function: however Sn2 reactions showed strict unit order in stoichiometric base concentration [60]. Apparently the change of activity of the solvent as the base concentration increases causes different solvation of the transition states of elimination and substitution, depending on the detailed distribution of charge, and so the olefin percentage may increase with base concentration in this range.

2. The Strength of the Base

All reagents capable of promoting elimination by either uni- or bi-molecular pathways can also promote substitution—*i.e.* they can show nucleophilicity towards both hydrogen and carbon**—and the olefin yield will be controlled by the relative discrimination for these atoms. Whether thermodynamic or kinetic control prevails will depend on the stability of the bonds between the reagent and carbon and hydrogen under the reaction conditions. Usually the latter type occurs, and this will be chiefly considered here, but if one of these bonds is labile, the step involving its formation may be reversible and the reaction may be channelled through the other pathway.

In theory, the partition between elimination and substitution for each mechanism-type can be determined by a calculation of the interaction energies for particular reactants. In practice, this goal is unattainable as yet, but a qualitative approach enables the known

---

* *E.g.* in 4 *M* NaOMe in MeOH, the ratio of solute to solvent molecules is about 1:4.

** In the following, unless otherwise specified, *basicity* and *nucleophilicity* will be used to express nucleophilicity towards hydrogen and carbon respectively.

data to be rationalised and certain predictions to be made. If we consider the reaction of a given substrate with different reagents in various solvents, we can neglect the influence of the leaving group, to a first approximation, and can assume that the reactivity of the reagent in both elimination and substitution will increase with

(1) a decrease of its solvation energy,
(2) an increase in the energy of the bond to be formed,
(3) an increase in the electrostatic attractions (both polarisation and polarisability) between the reactants,
(4) a decrease in the steric interactions between the reactants.

The last influences are probably only important for substitution at secondary or tertiary centres, and will be henceforth ignored.

These factors are not all independent. For instance, a decrease in solvation of an anion will increase its free energy, but it will also cause an increase in the electrostatic interactions with the atom to be attacked. All will depend on the detailed structure of the transition state and will usually differ in importance for the substitution and elimination processes of a pair of reactants. This implies that no universal order of nucleophilicity or of basicity is to be expected, although scales for restricted sets of conditions may be developed [61].

Detailed attempts to assess the relative importance of these factors are hampered by a lack of thermochemical and structural data, and we shall present a qualitative discussion using known or plausible relative magnitudes for the energy terms. As reactivity is very highly dependent on solvation effects, it is convenient to consider in turn the influence of factors (2) and (3) for various reagents in each of the main solvent types—strongly-solvating hydroxylic and poorly or differentially-solvating (see later) aprotic media [62]. More detail concerning the effect of variation of solvation within each of these classes is considered in section 3.

(a) Hydroxylic solvents

The favoured mechanisms for the reaction of a number of anions with typical halide and 'onium compounds in these media are shown in Table 4. The sequence, which ranges from very facile bimolecular reactivity through to complete unreactivity by this mechanism, is the same for any solvent of this class, and also is usually independent of the structure of the substrate, since the

TABLE 4

FAVOURED REACTIONS OF SOME NUCLEOPHILES
IN PROTIC SOLVENTS

B	Favoured mechanisms	pK_a (for HB)
$\overline{O}Alk$	E2, S_N2	$\geqslant 17$
$\overline{O}H$	E2, S_N2	16
$\overline{C}N$	S_N2	11
$\overline{O}Ph$	S_N2	10
$\overline{N}Me_3$	S_N2, little E2	10
$\overline{S}Ph$	E2, S_N2	7
$\overline{O}Ac$	S_N2, little E2	5
$\overline{F}$	Probably no bimolecular reaction	3
$\overline{N}O_3$	No bimolecular reaction	—1
$\overline{C}l$	S_N2	—7
$\overline{B}r$	S_N2	—9
$\overline{I}$	S_N2	—10
$\overline{C}lO_4$	No bimolecular reaction	—10

electronegativity and polarisability of the atom being attacked, or steric hindrance to such attack, are relatively unimportant.

Unfortunately, not enough data are available to draw up a kinetic scale of basicity under standard conditions, such as has been done for nucleophilicity towards carbon [61], but a qualitative idea of the affinity of a base B for a hydrogen atom which is bonded to carbon (and hence of factors (2) and (3)) can be obtained from the strength of the B–H bond of the conjugate acid in these media.

A measure of this is the pK_a value for the equilibrium *[29]*, in water, in which all the reactants are, of course, solvated. The weaker the BH bond, the stronger will be the acid and the smaller its pK_a.

$$B-H \rightleftharpoons \bar{B} + \overset{+}{H} \tag{29}$$

Conversely, the greater the affinity of B for a proton, the weaker will be the acid. The pK_a values for the conjugate acids of some potentially basic anions are given in Table 4 and, as the scale is logarithmic, the range of acidity is very large.

Base-catalysed reactions generally obey the Brönsted Law (30),

$$\log k_B = A.pK_a + B \tag{30}$$

where k_B is the catalytic constant and A and B are constant for a particular substrate and set of conditions. Presumably such a relation exists for E2 processes, and involves an A dependent on the electronegativity of the base and the nature of the transition state, and also for S_N2 reactions when, for a particular substrate, solvent etc., different A and B factors would be found. In the latter case the pK term would refer to the "carbon-basicity" *[62a]*. Recently, some Brönsted exponents have been measured for eliminations and have been interpreted on the basis of the structure of the transition state employed *[461]*.

The reagents which can promote E2 all do so irreversibly, for either a very strong bond to hydrogen is formed (*e.g.* in EtOH, H_2O), or, when this is not so (*e.g.* $\overset{+}{N}HMe_3$, PhOH), the back addition of acid to the olefin is very slow. Such anions also form strong bonds to carbon and S_N2 is also irreversible, and so the E2–S_N2 ratio is kinetically controlled.

The only bases of preparative importance are the alkoxides and hydroxide ion; and the order of efficiency of these (in the corresponding conjugate acid as solvent) is: $\bar{O}H < \bar{O}Me < \bar{O}Et < \bar{O}Pr^i. < \bar{O}Bu^t$, which is the same order as the pK_a values of the conjugate acids. As with all other anions in these media, the charge density on the most basic atom must be dispersed by hydrogen bonding to the solvent and this must have kinetic consequences. However, complete proton transfer is possible for these oxygen-containing anions and a negative charge can be passed through a solvent structure to the reaction site by a series of rapid proton transfers (such as causes the high mobility and ionic conductivity of protons) without the need for actual molecular diffusion. These bases can form strong bonds with both carbon and hydrogen, but they prefer to attack the usually more electrophilic hydrogen, probably because of the intense electrical field associated with these relatively unscreened peripheral atoms. The percentage of elimination, however, falls rapidly (cf. with $\overline{O}Ac$, $\overline{O}Ph$) when the latter bond becomes comparatively weak. A similar fall, in similar circumstances, occurs for NMe_3 and $\overline{C}N$.

An exact correspondence of kinetic affinities towards hydrogen and thermodynamic pK_a values would not be expected to exist in all cases and thiophenoxide ion in particular [63–65], and also other sulphur anions [66, 67], sometimes fall out of line. The former anion would be expected to be much less reactive in E2 than phenoxide or cyanide, for its conjugate acid is considerably stronger than those of the others; but whereas the last mentioned anions only give traces of elimination products, thiophenoxide often readily promotes such reactions, sometimes at a rate greater than that shown by hydroxide under the same conditions [63, 64].

These anions are also highly nucleophilic towards carbon, and their exceptional reactivity may be due to the high polarisability of the sulphur atom: the superior affinity for hydrogen in certain cases being due to the occurrence of particularly electrophilic hydrogens. A lack of solvation could also play some role, for sulphur nucleophiles are less hydrogen-bonded to the solvent than are most of the other anions to be considered: this would cause an all-round increase in reactivity. Solvation effects could be elucidated by kinetic studies in dipolar-aprotic solvents (see next section). Sometimes thiophenoxide is completely non-basic: e.g. 100 % substitution occurs with such apparently favourable substrates as $BrCH_2CH_2I$ and $(CH_3CHPh)_4\overset{+}{N}$ [68, 69], and here presumably the β-hydrogens are not the most electrophilic centres available. Another explanation which involves a special mechanism for these types of reagents is described in section 2c.

The anions of strong acids have negligible affinity for protons, but $\bar{C}l$, $\bar{B}r$ and $\bar{I}$ undergo S_N2 reactions more readily than alkoxides do under similar conditions, and this is again probably attributable to their polarisability and relative lack of deactivation by solvation [62]: the weakness of the bond formed to hydrogen must be responsible for the lack of elimination. Fluoride, which is the most strongly solvated halide ion and is also poorly polarisable, is unreactive towards both carbon and hydrogen even though it forms quite strong bonds to the former. Nitrate and perchlorate ions are also difficultly polarisable, quite strongly stabilised by solvation, and form weak bonds to both carbon and hydrogen: both are non-basic and non-nucleophilic, and so unimolecular mechanisms (when possible) can proceed by default.

This sequence of anion reactivity probably also holds for protic, but non-hydroxylic, solvents such as amines or amides; for instance, halide ions are strongly nucleophilic, but non-basic, in typical amides [62, 70].

The reagent only plays a passive role in the slightly activated E1 and the probably non-activated S_N1 processes and so there is little discrimination by different species between these two pathways. Anions or solvent molecules which accept protons will do so to form compounds which are acidic in protic solvents, e.g. HCl or $\overset{+}{E}tOH_2$ and readdition either of HX or of the elements of the solvent to the olefin may occur and an equilibrium be set up unless a stronger (but not E2-intervening) proton-absorber is present. The S_N1 component is usually solvolysis, and as this is often irreversible it may completely dominate the competing reversible E1.

The E1 step can be made completely irreversible in certain conditions, and an interesting example occurs in the alkylation of hydrocarbons in concentrated acids. This proceeds through carbonium ions but is hindered by much olefin formation and subsequent polymerisation from these intermediates if large concentrations of bisulphate, or other anions which are strong bases under these conditions, are present [71].

(b) Aprotic solvents

The importance of solvation in controlling the reactivity of a base, and hence the olefin yield, is well illustrated when the situation in these media is considered, for in many cases this factor appears predominant and the electrostatic and bond-energy terms are less important. Practically no quantitative kinetic data are available, but scattered reports, mainly from preparative studies, can be reasonably interpreted on this view. Now, anions cannot hydrogen-bond to solvent molecules and their free energy is increased (*cf.* the situation in protic media) by amounts dependent on the basicity of the donor atom. Bimolecular transition-states are destabilised to a lesser degree and to an extent not greatly dependent on the base used, and so the relative rates for different bases in the two types of medium are chiefly governed by the solvation of the anion in the initial states [62, 72]. Another important difference occurs in unimolecular processes, for solvolysis of a carbonium ion cannot usually occur and an anion-addition takes place which is often reversible: thus the path of reaction can often wholly be diverted to olefin formation if the acid which is formed in the E1 step is removed from the system by use of a proton-absorbing solvent (such as dimethylformamide) [73, 74], by the addition of an otherwise inert base (such as lutidine), or by the addition of a complexing agent (such as $\overline{Cl}$, which forms the relatively inert species $\overline{HCl_2}$ with eliminated HCl). A similar result can also be obtained in bimolecular reactions if the S_N2 step is reversible, but the E2 step is made irreversible by some similar stratagem [75].

The strongest bases in aprotic media are the anions derived from metal-alkyls and aryls, and Grignard reagents but these often promote unusual mechanisms which will be discussed in Chapter 4. Salts are usually insoluble in non-polar solvents such as benzene and carbon tetrachloride, which possess negligible solvating power, and even if solution occurred the reactivity would be diminished by ion-association; but dipolar solvents such as acetone, dimethyl-sulphoxide, or dimethylformamide possess higher dielectric constants and an exposed negative end of a dipole which can strongly solvate cations; and many salts are soluble and dissociated at low concentrations in these. The other end of the dipole is partially screened; labile, exchangeable hydrogens are not present; and so anions are not appreciably solvated or deactivated. The importance of this differential solvation has recently been demonstrated in S_N2 by the change in nucleophilic order $\bar{I} > \bar{Br} > \bar{Cl} > \bar{F}$ to the reverse when the solvent is changed from hydroxylic to dipolar-aprotic under otherwise identical conditions [62, 72]. The tendency of the halide ions to hydrogen-bond with the solvent, and so be deactivated, is the reverse of the order just quoted: thus fluoride, the anion of the most electronegative element, is outstanding in this capacity and is accordingly the least reactive in protic media. Such deactivation is not appreciable in dipolar-aprotics and the nucleophilicity of the relatively unsolvated ion is governed by its electrostatic interaction and capacity for bond-formation with the appropriate atom of the substrate, and this reactivity increases on changing from protic to aprotic media by magnitudes not explicable by any model of solvation that uses the dielectric constant of the medium as an index of solvating power.

This idea can be extended to elimination, for if an anion can powerfully bond to the solvent it should exhibit a large affinity for protons if placed in a solvent of no donating-ability and so might promote elimination from a substrate with suitably acidic β-hydrogens. Such an enhancement of elimination would generally be counteracted by a greater tendency to substitution, but if a reagent of high charge density and/or polarisability is chosen it might be hoped that hydrogen would be attacked rather than the generally less electrophilic carbon. The bond-energy factor might also be more favourable to elimination in these, rather than in hydroxylic solvents (*e.g.* with H–Hal).

In aprotic media, back-addition of the acid to the nascent olefin could occur; but in thermal decompositions and in other cases shortly to be mentioned, a volatile acid could be driven off or otherwise effectively removed from the system, and so an equilibrium displaced in favour of the olefin.

There are indications in the literature and in recent work which substantiate these views. The most likely anion is fluoride (which acts as a base in aqueous solution in certain enolisations) [76]*, but it is difficult to obtain evidence for its participation in olefin-formation because the alkyl fluorides which could be readily formed under the reaction conditions are well-known to eliminate on heating in the absence of bases, or especially in the presence of acids [77–79]. Suggestive, but thus inconclusive, are reports that up to 60% olefin together with alkyl fluorides are formed when alkali or mercuric fluorides are heated above 100° with alkyl halides, either alone [80], in dipolar-aprotics (with the devices to prevent the absorption of acid already noted) [75], or in glycol [81, 82]. A better example is the ready decomposition of $Et_4\overset{+}{N}F$ in chloroform or dipolar-aprotics at lower temperatures or in the absence of solvent at about 110° to give ethylene in excellent yield [83]—the other halide salts of this cation only form traces of olefin, together with much substitution products at above 200°. These reaction conditions, especially in solution, seem to be too mild for the ethylene to have originated from decomposition of pre-formed ethyl fluoride. Lithium fluoride in dimethylformamide has also been used as an efficient dehydrohalogenating agent for steroids [84].

There are many examples of chloride-promoted eliminations. Telomer iodides $CF_3(CF_2)_nCH_2CF_2I$ [85], alkyl [86] and cyclo-hexyl-halides [87] and tosylates [88], acetylated-aldose halides [89], and steroids [84, 90, 91] are all dehydrohalogenated with varying degrees of ease by lithium chloride in acetone and/or especially dimethylformamide. The last example is a well-known preparative method and has been briefly studied [92] with the conclusion that an E2 rather than a metal-ion catalysed or cyclic process prevails. Lithium chloride is the vogue because of its large solubility in these media (compared to KF, KCl etc.) and dimethyl-formamide is an excellent proton-absorbing solvent, but systematic kinetic and product studies with different metal halides and solvents would be worthwhile** and an added attraction from the preparative

---

* Fluoride ion has recently been found to act as a base in the Hofmann reaction [462].

** Co-ordination compounds of metal fluorides and organic ligands (such as dimethylsulphoxide) are soluble in dipolar aprotics, and should be useful in this context.

viewpoint is that the concurrent S_N2 reaction does not remove the substrate from the reaction, but merely converts it into another (inverted) halide, which can ultimately fall victim to a much slower irreversible elimination. Other anions, *e.g.* $\bar{Br}$, $\bar{I}$, $\bar{NO}_2$, and $\bar{CN}$, may possibly be capable of such reactions, but little data are available [73, 74, 93].

The idea that hydrogen-bonding and the levelling-effect of protic solvents could affect the basicity of oxygen-containing anions was vaguely realised some 20 years ago [94], since when several scattered observations of the enhanced reactivity of these ions in aprotic solvents have appeared. KOH pellets in mineral oil will dehydrohalogenate fluoro-carbons when all other methods fail [95]; *tert.*-butoxide ion is some 10^9-fold more basic in dimethylsulphoxide than in methanol as indicated from the rate of enolisation of ketones [96] and will promote elimination from sulphonium salts at room temperature [228]; and the elimination rates of a standard substrate with methoxide ion increase in the order of solvents (when corrected for the solubility of the salt); methanol < dimethylformamide ~ methyl cyanide ≪ acetone ≪≪ dioxan [97]. Hydroxide ion is well-known to show a basicity out of proportion to its concentration in pyrolyses where most of an aqueous solvent with its deactivating influence has been removed [98, 99]. One example is the observation that isobornyl 'onium salts decompose by the E1 mechanism in strongly alkaline aqueous conditions, as shown by the isolation of completely rearranged products (see Chap. 5, sect. 1), but on pyrolysis only give unrearranged bornylene by what must be an E2 reaction [100]. Another is that Hofmann degradation is often carried out in vacuo at low temperatures, so that all the solvent is removed before decomposition, and a superior yield of olefin is obtained than by the usual pyrolysis of a concentrated syrup [94]: in the latter case the presence of some solvent apparently discriminates against elimination, despite the favourable increase of temperature. The pyrolyses of the *n*-propyl 'onium salts of the weakly basic anions $\bar{O}Ac$, $\bar{Br}$, $\bar{Cl}$ and $\bar{O}Ph$ give only *ca.* 10% olefin [2, 101], but in the only cases studied for $\bar{F}$ ($Et_4\overset{+}{N}\bar{F}$) [83] and $\bar{CN}$ ($CH_3CHPh\overset{+}{N}Me_3C\bar{N}$) [102] almost quantitative olefin yields were achieved, and (but for the unpleasant by-products) these anions might rival the usual hydroxide in Hofmann Degradation. It would be interesting to observe the effect of the addition of a dipolar-aprotic solvent in these cases after the aqueous solvent had been removed but before pyrolysis.

Solvation effects are probably less important for uncharged organic bases, but some kinetic evidence for the expected variation of basicity in these solvents has been obtained [103], and pyridine [92] and collidine [84] in dimethylformamide have been used for highly effective dehydrohalogenations of steroids. When an aprotic organic base is used as the reaction medium, excellent olefin yields are obtained under brutal conditions [95, 104], eqn. (31) in reactions which could involve the initial formation of an 'onium salt and halide ion: but when the base contains an hydroxyl group and

$$n\text{-}C_8H_{17}Cl \xrightarrow[\text{at 180°}]{\text{B, 15 hours}} n\text{-}C_6H_{13}\cdot CH:CH_2$$

$$\tag{31}$$

B = NEt(Pri)$_2$, NEt(C$_6$H$_{11}$)$_2$ 100% olefin yield
B = NEt (CH$_2$CH$_2$OH)$_2$ 32% olefin yield

hydrogen-bonding becomes possible, substitution mainly occurs*. This is another example of the greater deactivation with respect to nucleophilicity towards hydrogen than towards carbon, which is caused by this solvation.

The principles which have been outlined in this section are not generally appreciated, for most ideas of basicity are framed in terms of experience with the common hydroxylic solvents. If these ideas were systematically applied, new fields in olefin synthesis could probably be opened. Especially interesting would be experiments using solutions of alkoxides in aqueous mixtures with dimethyl-sulphoxide, dimethylformamide, or tetramethylenesulphone.

(c) Merged mechanisms

Some other examples of eliminations occurring in unexpected situations have recently been unearthed. The reactions of cyclo-

---

* Elimination is also favoured by the steric requirements of the first two amines: these bases would attack an exposed hydrogen atom much more readily than a shielded carbon.

hexyldimethanesulphonates with chloride ion in alcohol give exclusive elimination *[88]* and 4-*tert.*-butylcyclohexyltoluene-sulphonate (-"tosylate") in acetone with supposedly non-basic halide and thiophenoxide anions gives up to 57% olefin *[105]*. In the former case an E2 reaction would not be expected, and in the latter such a mechanism, involving the anion, was ruled out by stereochemical considerations*, as also was a S_N2 reaction followed by elimination. A new type of process—"a merged mechanism of elimination and substitution"—was proposed *[105]* to accommodate the latter results, whereby either an intermediate with a 5-covalently bonded carbon that was similar to a S_N2 transition state or a transition state was formed and was partitioned between the two competing processes, eqn. (32). Either the attacking or the

Intermediate or   (32)
transition state

leaving group could abstract a β-proton in the event of elimination. This intermediate was only inferred, and not directly detected in any way.

The onus of initiating such a mechanism lies with the nucleo-philicity of the anion, and so the other example cited above and also the lithium chloride dehydrohalogenations and other elimi-nations which were considered in the last section might also be embraced by this scheme *[64, 93]*. Thus thiophenoxide is extremely nucleophilic towards carbon, and it has been suggested *[64]* that the extensive elimination, which occurs in the reaction of cyclo-alkyl *[64]* and steroid tosylates *[65]* with this and with thioacetate

---

* These may not be as weighty as was originally thought (see Chap. 6, sect. 4c).

ion in alcoholic media, is due to merged mechanisms rather than to the explanation given in sect. 2a. These anions are, however, usually completely non-basic towards acyclic compounds, and the restricted relative orientations of the leaving group and the β-hydrogen, such as occur in cyclic but not in straight-chain compounds, may be necessary to permit a merged process. On the other hand, it seems surprising that the partial formation of a strong C–S bond in any intermediate complex does not direct more of the reaction towards substitution.

It seems significant that cyclic tosylates are involved in most of the supposed merged mechanisms and cases where thiophenoxide ion shows basicity. Acyclic tosylates are rather unreactive in either E1 or E2 processes—in contract to their behaviour in S_N1 or S_N2—and even such favourable structures as the β-phenylethyl and sec-octyl compounds give low olefin yields [64, 106]. Cyclic tosylates, however, form much olefin with hydroxide or even acetate ions in aqueous solution [67, 107, 108]: thus it seems that the special mechanism may appear if a cyclic 6-membered transition state, eqn. (33) can be formed, but probably not for the

$$+ \bar{X} + HOSO_2R \qquad (33)$$

chloride-promoted dehydrohalogenations previously mentioned. It would be interesting to study the basicity of anions containing sulphur towards acyclic tosylates.

Quite good yields of olefin are obtained on solvolysis of cyclic tosylates especially in poorly solvating media [109, 257, 260]: here, elimination within an ion-pair may involve a cyclic transition state.

The merged process has been suggested [64] for only one acyclic example, in order to account for the large olefin yield obtained from the decomposition of tert.-butyl bromide with thio-anions in aqueous ethanol [63, 463]. This reaction could be an example of E2 or it may be more complex than was originally thought, but despite the large density of β-hydrogens about the leaving group there seems no reason to suspect a merged mechanism. Such a mechanism would have to overcome the considerable steric hindrance to the formation of an intermediate possessing a 5-co-ordinated carbon atom—hindrance which may inhibit normal S_N2 processes, for there is some evidence that *tert.*-butyl halides undergo E1 and readdition to give formal substitution products rather than S_N2 *[110, 111]*. If the existence of an intermediate complex is conceded, then a well-bonded thiophenoxide ion would mainly lead to substitution, rather than elimination, and a weakly-bonded ion (and in such a reactive solvent, the complex would be unstable) would give an olefin yield not much different from that of a normal E1 process. On either count, the 90% yield of olefin cannot be accommodated on the basis of the new mechanism.

The idea of merged mechanisms is interesting and in certain systems, especially the original cyclohexyl example, it seems possible, but at the moment there is insufficient supporting evidence for its indiscriminate application. Studies of ^{18}O isotope effects in the tosylate group and of β-deuterium effects would be worthwhile.

3. Solvent Effects

A change of solvent can affect the mechanism and also the rates of competing substitution and elimination in a more general manner than was considered in the preceding sections, and attention will now be focussed on the stability of the transition state of a particular type of reaction in different media. The situation is too complex to be treated quantitatively, but Hughes and Ingold have developed *[3]* a qualitative approach, based on a simple model of solvation, which assumes that the stabilisation due to interaction with the medium increases with the charge density on the species considered; and this theory holds very well for the decomposition of 'onium compounds and halides in protic solvents. Much more data are known for the effect of solvent change on substitution rate than on elimination, and several semi-quantitative theories have been developed for the former class. These treatments have very re-

stricted predicative value and, as they do not deal specifically
with elimination, they will not be discussed here: recent summaries
are available *[25, 110]*.

(a) The effect on mechanism

A change to a more polar medium will favour or hinder unimolecular processes according to the charge on the substrate.
Ionisation of neutral compounds (*cf.* eqn. (34)) is mainly promoted
by electrophilic attack by solvent molecules on the negative end
of the forming ion-pair, since the solvation energy of an anion is
usually greater than that of a cation (and the solvation of a carbonium ion is much less than that of an inorganic cation); however,
nucleophilic stabilisation of the developing positive charge by the
solvent also plays a part. As a result, amphoteric solvents (water,
alcohols) are particularly good ionising media for neutral substrates, and ionisation occurs more easily in acidic solvents (which
possess electrophilic hydrogen atoms), than in basic ones (which
cannot easily solvate anions). Such facile solvation, mainly by

$$R\text{---}X \longrightarrow \overset{\delta+}{R} \dots \overset{\delta-}{X} \longrightarrow \overset{+}{R} + \overset{-}{X} \tag{34}$$

$$R\text{---}\overset{+}{X} \longrightarrow \overset{\delta+}{R} \dots \overset{\delta+}{X} \longrightarrow \overset{+}{R} + X \tag{35}$$

hydrogen-bonding, of a transition state in which charge is being
created usually implies a medium of high dielectric constant; but
this is not invariably so, for hydrogen cyanide, which has a dielectric
constant of about 115, is a poorer solvating medium, as judged from
its capacity to dissolve salts, than is acetic acid, which has a corresponding value of 6. Aqueous–organic mixtures, nitromethane,
acetic and formic acids, and liquid sulphur dioxide all possess the
desired properties to a greater or lesser, but nevertheless an
adequate extent, and secondary and tertiary alkyl halides and
arylsulphonates readily decompose in them to form ion-pairs:
whether further dissociation to free ions occurs depends on the dielectric constant as well as on the solvating power. Poorly solvating
media, such as ethers, hydrocarbons, and most aromatics, do not

assist ionisation and unimolecular processes do not usually occur.

An ionic substrate will have quite different requirements, for the charge is dispersed in the transition state leading to heterolysis, eqn. (35). Desolvation will thus occur on passing into this state and the more powerfully solvating the medium, the more difficult this will be, and the more stabilised will be the initial state compared to the transition state. The comments in the previous paragraph about cation solvation refer to carbonium ions, but in the case of interest now—ammonium and sulphonium ions, particularly the former—the charge will be more largely localised on a non-carbon atom, and so more extensive stabilisation will result. Ionisation of these substrates will only occur in weakly solvating media—as in the example of $C_2H_5\overset{+}{N}Me_3\bar{I}$ which shows no trace of unimolecular decomposition in water or ethanol at 160° and 100° respectively, but undergoes just detectable reaction in tert.-butanol at the lower temperature [79]. As ammonium compounds have a greater charge-density on the 'onium atom than have sulphonium compounds, they are more heavily solvated under similar conditions, and do not undergo E1 reactions as easily*. In fact they are so stabilised by almost any medium which will dissolve them, that it is only when the C–N bond is weakened by steric compression [14d], by methoxy-substituted α-phenyl substituents [112, 113], or by driving forces of rearrangement [100] (as in the isobornyl case mentioned in sect. 2b), that such mechanisms have been reported in water or ethanol; although, no doubt, they could be frequently achieved by the use of low-polar solvents, and indeed may have been recently obtained in pyridine [114]. Dipolar aprotic solvents, which can only effectively solvate cations, have been little studied with reference to their capacity for permitting ionisation, but they should not be very favourable media for neutral substrates and should stabilise 'onium salts, perhaps more so than hydroxylic solvents.

When little nucleophilic assistance to ionisation is provided by the medium, the maximum intramolecular neighbouring-group and

---

* The C–N bond energy (in the absence of solvent) is actually less than that for C–S.

electronic assistances for electron release to the α-carbon atom are evoked in what can been termed "limiting-conditions" [115]. In bimolecular reactions the departure of the leaving group is also assisted by the bond formation with the attacking base, and so in a solvent which disfavours a particular charge-type these reactions will occur more easily than unimolecular processes.

(b) The effect on rate

The variation of rate and olefin yield for solvent change within a given mechanism must also be discussed in terms of the charge-type of the reactants. There are 4 cases to consider for E2 mechanisms, as the reagent can either be negatively charged or neutral, and the substrate can be positively charged or neutral. Typical examples of each of these are shown in A to D. The second step of an El can similarly involve a neutral or a negative reagent.

(A) $O\bar{H} + CH_3CH_2Br \longrightarrow H_2O + CH_2:CH_2 + \bar{B}r$

(B) $NMe_3 + (CH_3)_3CBr \longrightarrow H\overset{+}{N}Me_3 + CH_2:C(CH_3)_2 + \bar{B}r$

(C) $\bar{O}Et + CH_3CH_2\overset{+}{S}Me_2 \longrightarrow EtOH + CH_2:CH_2 + SMe_2$

(D) $H_2O + NO_2\langle\hspace{-4pt}\bigcirc\hspace{-4pt}\rangle CH_2CH_2\overset{+}{N}Me_3 \longrightarrow H_3\overset{+}{O} + NO_2\langle\hspace{-4pt}\bigcirc\hspace{-4pt}\rangle CH:CH_2 + NMe_3$

In types A and D there is no net change of charge after reaction, but for C charge is destroyed and for B it is created. On the basis of these relations, Hughes and Ingold have developed their theory of solvent effects. They compare the charge distribution in the reactants and in the transition state and make the reasonable assumption that processes involving charge formation or destruction, on going into the transition state, are more drastically affected by solvation than those involving charge dispersion. This viewpoint is equivalent to predicting the effect of solvation on the activity coefficients in the rate expression (36) (in which the conventional

$$\text{Rate} = k_0\,[B]\,[S]\,\frac{f_B f_S}{f^{\neq}} \tag{36}$$

symbols are used) and where the species are neutral or charged, depending on the types A to D; but as very little is known about the magnitude of these quantities, we will adopt a more qualitative approach. All the E1 and E2 types have been considered in detail from this viewpoint, and here only one example will be given. The distribution of charge in the transition states for the E2 and S_N2 processes of a type A reaction are shown in (XVIII) and (XIX),

$$\overset{\delta-}{B}\cdots H \cdots \overset{|}{C}_\beta \overset{|}{-\!-}\overset{|}{C}_\alpha \cdots \overset{\delta-}{X} \qquad\qquad \overset{\delta-}{B}\cdots \overset{|}{C}_\alpha \cdots \overset{\delta-}{X}$$

(XVIII)   (XIX)

and the total charge in each transition state is the same, for charge is conserved in this sub-group, but it is dispersed in comparison with the distribution in the initial state. The effect of more solvation would thus be to stabilise the initial state with respect to both transition states by a relatively small amount (relative, that is, to a case in which charge was destroyed altogether), and so both substitution and elimination should show a slightly smaller rate on changing to a more polar (or strictly, a more solvating) medium. The dispersal of charge in (XVIII) is spread over more atoms than in the other case, and so in addition stabilisation of the transition state of elimination should be somewhat less than that for substitution, and so the olefin yield should slightly fall on making the solvent change just described.

By analogous reasoning, predictions for the other types can be made as these are in Table 5. The terms large and small, which by experiment are found to represent rate changes of greater or less than about ten-fold, are a result of the conclusion that differences of charge magnitude are more important than are differences of charge distribution. The queries in the last column are cases where a prediction cannot be made, for charge is not conserved in these reactions, and the magnitude of the charges in the two competing transition states need not be the same. The theory is too qualitative to support a more detailed analysis of charge

TABLE 5

SOLVENT EFFECTS PREDICTED BY THE HUGHES-INGOLD THEORY

Type	Mechanism	Charge in T.S.	Effect of increasing solvation	
			on rate (total)	on olefin yield
(A) $\bar{B} + R—X$	S_N2, E2	Dispersed	Small decrease	Small decrease
(B) $B + R—X$	S_N2, E2	Increased	Large increase	?
(C) $\bar{B} + R—\overset{+}{X}$	S_N2, E2	Reduced	Large decrease	?
(D) $B + R—\overset{+}{X}$	S_N2, E2	Dispersed	Small decrease	Small decrease
$R—X$	S_N1, E1 ionisation step	Increased	Large increase	—
$R—\overset{+}{X}$	S_N1, E1 ionisation step	Dispersed	Small decrease	—
$\overset{+}{R} + \bar{B}$	S_N1, E1 product step	Reduced	—	?
$\overset{+}{R} + B$	S_N1, E1 product step	Dispersed	—	Small decrease

distribution as considered for the various transition state structures discussed in Chap. 1, sect. 3.

This theory only refers to effects on the activation energy, but also the entropy of activation must be affected, for a reduced or dispersed charge in the transition state will evoke less solvation, as compared with the initial state, and so, as an individual molecular reaction progresses, some solvent molecules will be released from their orientated positions in the solvation shell and an increase of entropy of the system would be expected, which would probably be large enough to overcome any negative contribution from restrictions involving the actual bond-structure of the reactants. The converse would occur if charge were created. According to the absolute rate theory, the rate coefficient of a reaction is dependent upon entropy change in the transition state as shown in eqn. (37), in which the usual symbols are used, and so positive and negative changes cause acceleration and retardation respectively. In practice,

$$\text{Rate coefficient} = \frac{kT}{h} \, e^{\frac{\Delta S^*}{R}} \, e^{\frac{-\Delta H^{\ddagger}}{RT}} \tag{37}$$

the magnitude and even direction of such entropy contributions are often difficult to predict. Certainly, the heat and entropy of activation should run parallel in size (but have opposite effects on the rate), for a large change of charge requires both large electrostatic energy-changes and the operation or relaxation of powerful orientating influences. But although it might be thought that the greater the polarity of the medium the larger would be the number of molecules, either released from or constrained to restricted orientations, and so the greater should be the entropy change; the degree of order in the bulk of the solvent must also be considered [116]. The bonded molecules of solvation may be less restricted than they would be in a surrounding highly organised solvent structure, and if this occurs, desolvation would introduce more order into the system.

Despite these uncertainties, the energy effect seems to predominate, for Ingold has shown [1] that his theory predicts the correct rate trends for all charge-types of 'onium salt and halides in protic media, with few exceptions. In few cases have the activation parameters of eqn. (37) been determined for a particular reaction in different pure solvents, but some examples are in Table 6. For the first two compounds cited, the rate is greater in the less polar tert.-butanol, as is expected from energy considerations, but this is the result of an acceleration of 10^4, favoured by the change in $\Delta H^{\ddagger}$, on passing to this solvent countered by a retardation of 10^3-fold, due to the entropy term. For the last example, the reaction is slower in water than in ethanol, as expected, but it

TABLE 6

HEAT AND ENTROPY FACTORS FOR E2 REACTIONS

Compound	System	$\Delta H^{\ddagger}$ (kcal.mole^{-1})	ΔS^{*} (e.u.)	Ref.
PhCH$_2$CH$_2$OTs	$\overline{O}$Et, EtOH	20.4	—11.2	106
	t-Bu$\overline{O}$, t-BuOH	14.7	—25.2	106
PhCH$_2$CH$_2$Br	$\overline{O}$Et, EtOH	20.4	— 6.8	44
	t-Bu$\overline{O}$, t-BuOH	13.0	—25.0	106
PhCH$_2$CH$_2$$\overset{+}{S}Me_2$$\overline{I}$	$\overline{O}$H, H$_2$O	24.0	— 4.2	116
	$\overline{O}$Et, EtOH	23.3	+ 7.7	116

would not have been expected that this is almost entirely due to the unfavourable entropy contribution in the former conditions. This must be an example of the influence of a highly ordered solvent, but such a situation, although possible in water, would probably not occur in organic solvents for which more positive entropy changes would be expected with more solvating media. However, more data for decompositions in pure solvents are required, before the extent of such occurrences can be judged. The parameters obtained in mixed solvents are difficult to interpret because of the likelihood of solvation by the more polar component out of proportion to its concentration: thus a few percent of water in a solvent, such as dioxan, can solvate a solute present in low concentration almost as effectively as a much more aqueous solvent.

A quantitative theory of these effects is not possible at the present time. The basis of any such method would be to determine the charge distribution in the initial and transition states and then to calculate the free-energy change to achieve the latter in solvents of different polarity: but the former problem has not yet been solved, and the other part requires a detailed knowledge of the laws governing short-range forces in media of differing macroscopic dielectric constant and the problems of preferential solvation for mixed solvents; and these are imperfectly understood. However, the predictions in Table 5 are in qualitative accord with those that have been made on the basis of semi-empirical theories of the solvent dependence of rate for ion-ion and ion-dipole reactions [117]. Even rough quantitative agreement would not be anticipated, for such theories only apply to solvents of considerably higher dielectric constant (> 40) than those used for most elimination studies.

There have been criticisms of the Hughes-Ingold theory. Most of the supporting data for elimination have been obtained for aqueous-alcoholic solutions of varying compositions, and it has been claimed that in such media the activities of typical substrates vary in an irregular and unpredictable manner such as to make any rate trends appear fortuitous [118]. Also the use of alkali hydroxides in such solvents causes an equilibrium with alkoxide to be set up, and the relative concentrations of the two anions are reported [119, 120] to vary appreciably with small medium charges especially near the limits of the solvent composition scale (*i.e.* near to 100% alcohol or 100% water), and so a change of rate could be due to a change in basic reagent, rather than to solvation phenomena. In this case the use of aqueous solutions of an inert (but polar) solvent, such as acetonitrile or dimethylformamide, might be advantageous; but even if both of the above effects could account for small rate differences, they cannot be responsible for the large changes often observed, which must be essentially due to solvation. It is easy to raise objections to the theory, but a superior one has not been offered, and for hydroxylic solvents it has good predicative value.

When aprotic solvents are considered a different situation arises, for here, as previously explained, the dielectric constant is not even an approximate index of the solvating power, and specific interactions between the solvent and reactants must be considered. A S_N2 reaction of charge-type A shows an increase of rate (after making allowance for the differences of dissociation of the reagent) of several thousand-fold on passing from ethanol to acetone, which is much larger than would be ascribed on the basis of the difference of dielectric constants of these solvents: a similar but presumably smaller effect should also occur for elimination. Dipolar aprotics can only effectively solvate cations, and so any reactions, in which positive charge is created, should be facilitated by such media, and those in which such charge is reduced, or dispersed, should be hindered. Not enough data are available to test these predictions.

4. Salt Effects

The addition of inert salt, or a variation in the concentrations of ionic reactants, can give rise to a primary salt effect by changing the activity coefficient term in eqn. (36) in a manner equivalent to that caused by changing the solvating power of the medium. A secondary effect, common-ion retardation, can occur for E1 reactions, and has already been considered.

The gross features of the primary effect seem to follow the theory as developed for solvation: for example type C reactions show a large rate decrease, with an increase of reactant concentration, but the effect on the two competing reactions seems identical, for the olefin proportion does not change over 8-fold variations in the ionic-strength of the medium [34]. Only a few quantitative studies have been carried out for E2 reactions, and although a plot of the logarithm of the rate in alcohol or water against the square root of the ionic-strength is linear to surprisingly high concentrations, the graphs do not have the theoretical slope [79, 121]. This is hardly unexpected, for the 'onium ions used are far from possessing a concentrated, spherically-distributed charge.

The situation is more complex in non-polar solvents and the "solvation" provided by added inert molecules can assist ionisation, or a synchronous elimination, in a manner best regarded as specific electrophilic catalysis, similar to that provided by silver or mercury cations towards organic halides in hydroxylic and other media.

5. The Effect of Temperature

Of two competing reactions, the one with the larger activation energy will prevail at high temperatures, and so any difference in this value between the elimination and substitution of a particular substrate, will cause a variation in the olefin yield with temperature. Such a variation is indeed found and it is best attributed to solvation effects.

This temperature-dependence for some typical examples is interpreted in Table 7 in terms of the eqn. (37). The last entry shows the entropy change expected for a "normal" bimolecular reaction—the mode for reactions between uncharged substrates. In all these cases the heat of activation for elimination is from 1 to 2 kcal.mole^{-1} greater than for the corresponding substitution, and this is either due to less solvation and consequently less stabilisation of the more dispersed charge in the former transition state, or (for 'onium compounds) to the need to start breaking the strong C_β–H bond before much energetic assistance from double-bond formation occurred (cf. E2 transition state, type A). The entropy change is always

TABLE 7

THE ARRHENIUS PARAMETERS $\Delta H^{\ddagger}$ AND ΔS^*
FOR E2 REACTIONS

($\Delta H^{\ddagger}$ is in kcal.mole^{-1}; ΔS^* in entropy units)

Reaction	Solvent	SN2		E2		Ref.
		ΔS^*	$\Delta H^{\ddagger}$	ΔS^*	$\Delta H^{\ddagger}$	
i-PrBr + $\overline{O}$Et	60% EtOH	—17.5	20.2	—12.9	21.5	3
β-PhenylethylBr + $\overline{O}$Et	100% EtOH	No reaction		— 9.2	19.6	3
t-BuS$\overset{+}{M}$e$_2$ + $\overline{O}$Et	100% EtOH	No reaction		+ 7.9	23.6	3
EtS$\overset{+}{M}$e$_2$ + $\overline{O}$Et	100% EtOH	+11.0	27.5	+16.6	30.0	34,79
n-PrS$\overset{+}{M}$e$_2$ + $\overline{O}$Et	100% EtOH	+11.5	28.2	+15.1	30.2	34,79
NeohexylS$\overset{+}{M}$e$_2$ + $\overline{O}$Et	100% EtOH	+15.6	28.7	No reaction		34,79
α-PhenylethylS$\overset{+}{M}$e$_2$ + $\overline{O}$Et	100% EtOH	+ 6.9	24.2	+17.0	26.3	34,79
β-PhenylethylS$\overset{+}{M}$e$_2$ + $\overline{O}$Et	100% EtOH	No reaction		+ 7.7	23.3	34,79

"Normal bimolecular", ΔS^* is —10 to —6 e.u.

more favourable to elimination (again attributable to solvation), but at available temperatures this cannot often counter-act the heat factor, and so elimination is usually the minor reaction. The general situation, to which there is probably only one exception [122], is that an increase in temperature increases the olefin proportion. An example of this is the ethoxide-promoted decomposition of ethyldimethylsulphonium ion which gives 14, 16, 20, and 21 % ethylene at 35°, 45°, 64°, and 73° respectively [34].

Another feature of the data available is that the entropy term for elimination or substitution of 'onium salts is always from 15 to 25 units more positive than that of normal bimolecular reactions, such as alkyl halides exhibit. This large change is undoubtedly due to solvation effects, rather than to any loosening of bonds in the reactants, for the ionic substrate and the base molecule both possess a large capacity for orientating solvent molecules which have to be released on entering the transition state, and such desolvation occurs to a much less extent with neutral compounds. A part of the large entropy and energy terms for 'onium compounds could be an artefact since the temperature is not the only variable, but the dielectric constant (and also presumably the solvating power of the medium) falls, as the temperature is increased. This would have a large effect on a reaction involving ions, and the net result would tend to increase the rate at high temperatures, relative to that in an isodielectric solvent, and so to give apparently high $\Delta H^{\ddagger}$ and ΔS^* values. Calculations and experiments for substitutions [117] indicate that if this effect is allowed for, the entropy charge might drop almost to the region of zero, and the heat term by several kcal.mole^{-1}. Experiments in mixtures of fixed dielectric constant (with a large excess of the more polar component, in order to eliminate preferential solvation), rather than of fixed composition, are necessary to evaluate this effect. It would also be interesting to obtain the parameters for reactions of charge types B and D (about which nothing is known), in order to establish the contribution made to the heat and entropy terms by the basic reagent in the cases previously considered.

The Arrhenius parameters for the ionisation of tertiary halides are in the range 22.3–24.0 kcal.mole^{-1} and $+1$ to -5 e.u.: the latter being as expected for "normal" unimolecular processes. For 'onium compounds, the corresponding figures are 31.0–33.0 and about $+18$ respectively, and the differences from the halides can again be readily attributed to solvation [1, 3]. The actual values for the elimination and substitution steps are not directly measurable, but their difference can be deduced from the variation of olefin yield with temperature as discussed in Chap. 1, sect. 1c. As shown there, the activation energy for elimination is small, but quite a large variation of product composition with temperature occurs: in the case of tert.-butyl chloride in 80% aqueous ethanol a 17, 24, and 36% yield of butylene [3] is obtained at 25°, 50°, and 65°.

When the effect of structural change on the velocity of both E1 and E2 reactions is studied, it is found that the individual $\Delta H^{\neq}$ and ΔS^{*} values do not correlate with structural variations as well as do the actual rate constants, especially for small ($\sim 10^2$-fold) ranges of rate: this is expected from theoretical considerations [45]. The fact that the rates do correlate in a systematic manner is rather surprising, for, as explained above, a large fraction of the factors controlling them is due to solvation influences, which might well be expected to vary irregularly over a few kcal.mole^{-1} for different structures*; but apparently this is not so, and the combined effect of the energy and entropy of solvation terms must be nearly constant for a homologous series of compounds.

6. Conditions for Maximum Olefin Yield

Much effort was expended by early workers in determining the best conditions for the preparation of olefins. It was generally agreed that primary halides gave the poorest yields, but the relative order of the secondary and tertiary compounds gave rise to much controversy because the importance of mechanism was not realised. Hughes and Ingold pointed out [1, 3] that primary halides invariably reacted by the E2 mechanism in the usual preparative

---

* Especially in view of the large solvation energy required to permit ionisation in the liquid phase (approx. 120–140 kcal. mole^{-1}).

conditions, but that the secondary and tertiary compounds could also undergo E1 processes. As the base concentration was increased or the solvent polarity was decreased, a tertiary halide could sustain such a mechanism under conditions whereby a secondary compound changed over to E2, but ultimately under very basic non-polar conditions, even the former type of compound would change mechanism. As the olefin yield from an E2 mechanism is greater than that from an E1, mainly because of the extreme facility of the solvolysis which competes with the latter, and as reasons, to be discussed later, favour a facilitation of E2 over S_N2 in the order, tertiary > secondary > primary, it can be understood that, under certain conditions, when a secondary halide reacted E2, but a tertiary E1, the former would give a larger olefin yield; but when both reacted E2, the latter would do so.

It follows from the discussion in the previous sections that for a maximum olefin yield from a given compound, and also to avoid rearrangement or other complications implicit in carbonium-ion formation, it is desirable to ensure an E2 reaction; and the traditional recipe (hot, strong, alcoholic potash) is a concentrated basic solution in a relatively non-polar solvent which is favourable for this, at a high temperature in order to take advantage of the favourable temperature coefficient of elimination with respect to substitution. This applies to both 'onium and halide compounds. An excellent method for halides involves prolonged refluxing with a high-boiling amine (sect. 2b): here all the above recommendations are utilised, especially the temperature effect.

Chapter 3

ORIENTATION RULES
AND THEIR INTERPRETATION

The study of the effect of structure on the mechanism of elimination was stimulated by two empirical rules which summarised the proportions of products obtained from reactions that could give different or isomeric olefins [123]. In the second half of the last century, Hofmann found that ethylene was almost exclusively formed when a quaternary ammonium hydroxide containing ethyl and other groups was decomposed, eqn. (38). This observation

$$CH_3CH_2\overset{+}{N}CH_2CH_2CH_3 \underset{\overset{|}{Me} \quad \overset{|}{Me}}{\xrightarrow{\overline{O}H}} CH_2:CH_2 (98\%) + CH_3CH:CH_2 (2\%) \quad (38)$$

was later generalized [2] to the effect that, the olefin predominately obtained from such compounds, is that which contains the smallest number of alkyl groups situated about the double bond.

Some years later, Saytzeff discovered that the isomer formed in major yield from the base-promoted decomposition of secondary and tertiary alkyl halides was such that the hydrogen atom was lost from the β-carbon possessing fewest such atoms, eqn. (39).

$$CH_3CH_2CHBrCH_3 \xrightarrow{\overline{O}H} CH_3CH:CHCH_3 (81\%) + CH_3CH_2CH:CH_2 (19\%)$$
$$(39)$$

This means that the olefin having most alkyl substituents about the double bond is the favoured product. The former rule has been found to apply to the E2 decompositions of sulphones, ammonium, and sulphonium salts and the latter to those of halides and sulphonate esters, to E1 processes in general, and also to the dehydration of alcohols. In most cases considerable amounts of the minor olefin products are also obtained. The interpretation of these diametrically opposed orientation rules required an understanding of the factors which controlled the rates of elimination in homologous series and in α-branched compounds, and it was found that substituents could exhibit polar effects of different time dependence which could give rate sequences compatible with either rule, depending on the mechanism and the substrate-type.

1. The Hofmann Rule

This rule implies that the least stable olefin is formed, for at temperatures below about 400° the most stable isomer of a given compound, or member of a homologous series, is the one with most alkyl substituents about the double bond. Factors which govern the stabilities of the possible end-products thus cannot be important in the transition states leading to Hofmann-type products.

The rule applies under strongly basic conditions and in 1927 Ingold and Hanhart generalised and explained [2] it as a consequence of the inductive effect of alkyl groups influencing the reactivity of the β-hydrogen atom to be eliminated. The substrate of reaction (38), which is the simplest 'onium compound that can form two olefins, was assumed to be polarised as in (XX), whereby

$$CH_3 \longrightarrow \overset{\delta\delta\delta+}{\underset{\underset{\beta'}{\overset{|}{H}}}{CH}} \longrightarrow \overset{\delta+}{CH_2} \longrightarrow \overset{+}{N} \longleftarrow \overset{\delta+}{CH_2} \longleftarrow \overset{\delta\delta+}{\underset{\underset{\beta}{\overset{|}{H}}}{CH_2}}$$

$$(XX)$$

the formally charged nitrogen atom induced a positive charge on the neighbouring α- and β-carbon atoms (the direction of electron drift being shown by the arrows) which in turn loosened their bonded hydrogens and in particular made β-hydrogens acidic and more available for elimination. If, however, the induced charge on the β-carbon was partially neutralised by the inductive electron-release of an attached alkyl group, the inductive effect of the 'onium atom was not fully relayed and so these β'-hydrogens were less acidic than those in the other β-branch. This polarisation exists in the ground state of the substrate, and on reaction the base preferentially attacks the more acidic hydrogen to give elimination in the direction shown according to the Hofmann rule.

A positive charge can influence remote atoms by electrical transmission through a carbon-chain as here described, and also by induction through space in the so-called direct- or field-effect [124]. The direct effect is always included in the generic term "inductive effect" as far as orientating influences are concerned, for both effects have the same source and the same consequences, and their separate influences are difficult to disentangle.

A similar explanation can be given for all the other known examples if allowance is made for the relative importance of the inductive effects of substituents in the branches, and for the electron-withdrawing powers of the formally-charged sulphur atoms in sulphonium compounds and sulphones. Expressed in modern terms, a transition state of type A (Chap. 1, sect. 3) is assumed, the stability of which is characterised by the acidity of the β-hydrogens and is influenced by factors which affect this, but which is relatively unaffected by the steric or conjugative properties of substituents.

The inductive effects of alkyl groups increase with homology in a manner that is well-established from studies of acid-strengths and dipole-moments [1] to be:

$$t\text{-Bu} > i\text{-Pr} \sim \text{higher } prim\text{-alkyl} > n\text{-Pr} > \text{Et} > \text{Me}$$

and as a large inductive effect of a β-substituent reduces the tendency for elimination, the order of reactivity in structures, for which the above groups are β-linked, should to be the reverse of this. Early results on the yield of olefin and the proportions of isomers from the thermal decompositions of compounds $R\overset{+}{N}Me_3\overline{O}H$ and $RR'\overset{+}{N}Me_2\overline{O}H$ [2, 125] and the corresponding sulphonium salts [126] were in accord with Ingold's theory, and recent work [34, 127], under kinetically controlled E2 conditions, has shown that the individual elimination rates also exhibit inductive control (Table 8). The increasing homology of the β-linked group causes a gradually increasing inductive effect and an elimination rate which smoothly falls towards a limit—if the last entry is omitted. The low rate value associated with a β-linked *tert.*-butyl group will be

TABLE 8

E2 RATES FOR 'ONIUM COMPOUNDS $RCH_2CH_2\overset{+}{X}$ [34]

(k_2 in sec^{-1}.mole^{-1})

Alkyl Compound β-Group (R)	Et H	n-Pr Me	n-Bu Et	n-Decyl n-C$_8$H$_{17}$	i-Pentyl i-Pr	i-Bu 2 × Me	neo-Hexyl t-Bu
$10^5 k_2$ A	79	29	21	—	16	10	0.4
B	71	5	3	2.6	1	2	0.08

A: $RCH_2CH_2\overset{+}{S}Me_2\bar{O}Et$ in EtOH at 101°.
B: $RCH_2CH_2\overset{+}{N}Me_2\bar{O}Et$ in EtOH at 64°.

considered later. The spread of rates for a given structural change is larger for the ammonium than for the sulphonium series and so the former shows stricter adherence to the Hofmann rule. It should be noted that the Hofmann order holds even when a statistical correction is made for the differing numbers of β-hydrogens—it is not valid to argue that the differing abundance of hydrogen is a major factor contributing to the Hofmann pattern of influences.

The orientation of elimination can still be explained by inductive control when β-substituents other than alkyl groups are present. In compounds $XCH_2CH_2\overset{+}{N}Me_2CH_2CH_3$ (X = Ph, Hal, OH, NH$_2$), the effect of X is to withdraw electrons from the β-carbon and so to loosen the attached hydrogens and to favour elimination in this branch [2, 125], rather than into the simpler ethyl branch as would have been expected on the basis of Hofmann's original statement.

The rule also applies to the branches of secondary and tertiary 'onium compounds under E2 conditions: this is illustrated by the relative rates of elimination from iso-propyl, sec.-butyl, tert.-butyl, and tert.-pentyl 'onium ethoxides in ethanol at 45°.

Relative rate for

$$CH_3—CH—CH_3 \qquad CH_3CH_2—CH—CH_3$$
$$\qquad | \qquad\qquad\qquad\qquad\qquad |$$
$$\oplus SMe_2 \qquad\qquad\qquad\qquad \oplus SMe_2$$

Propylene via E2	= 1.00
Butene-1 via E2	= 0.98
Butene-2 via E2	= 0.36

$$\qquad CH_3 \qquad\qquad\qquad\qquad\qquad CH_3$$
$$\qquad | \qquad\qquad\qquad\qquad\qquad\qquad |$$
$$CH_3—C—CH_3 \qquad CH_3CH_2—C—CH_3$$
$$\qquad | \qquad\qquad\qquad\qquad\qquad\qquad |$$
$$\oplus SMe_2 \qquad\qquad\qquad\qquad \oplus SMe_2$$

Isobutylene via E2	= 1.00
2-Methylbutene-1	= 0.89
2-Methylbutene-2	= 0.30

These results cannot be explained on the basis of the inductive effect alone, for although the least substituted olefin is predominately formed there is a large rate increase on passing from the primary to the secondary and tertiary series—*cf.* Table 10, next section—and in terms of the inductive effect the α-methylation should cause a slight retardation of reaction, not a considerable acceleration.

This additional dependence of rate on complexity of structure occurs in other cases: it is found that 'onium salts possessing two olefin-forming branches, one of which contains an α-alkyl group, decompose with *anti*-Hofmann orientation. Thus ethylisopropyl-dimethylammonium hydroxide yields 60% propylene rather than the expected major fraction of ethylene, and several other examples are included in a recent compilation of Hofmann degradations [34]. It does not seem to be generally appreciated that the Hofmann rule applies only to compounds with β-substituted side-chains.

This effect of α-groups must reflect the structure of the transition state which is utilised. Ethyl and other primary 'onium compounds almost certainly possess an E1cB-like transition state (type A) under typical degradation conditions, but with progressive α-methylation the tendency for C–X heterolysis increases and the transition state changes towards the more concerted type B. Although the acidity of the β-hydrogens is still dominant, and so Hofmann-type orientation is followed, the factors which can stabilise the developing double bond, such as α-alkyl groups (for an explanation see the next section), will now facilitate the reaction. The ammonium compounds would be expected to show less tendency for a type B transition state than sulphonium salts, for

the former do not undergo E1 reactions under conditions where
the latter readily do so; and a much smaller spread of rate as
α-branching occurs and also a much greater tendency to Hofmann
orientation for secondary or tertiary compounds is indeed found
for them.

The positive charge induced on the β-hydrogens is quite small.
Recent calculations [34] for 'onium compounds indicate that it is
often about $+0.02e$ (where e is the value of the electronic charge),
and differences between homologues of a tenth of this can cause
differences in the free energy of activation (as calculated on a
simple electrostatic model) of about 1 kcal.mole^{-1}: in general such
calculations are in good agreement with experiment. For halides
the induced charges are slightly smaller and show less variations
between corresponding homologues.

2. The Saytzeff Rule

Kinetic investigations have shown that this rule applies to the E2
reactions of secondary and tertiary halides and esters and to all
E1 reactions in which proton-loss occurs from a carbonium ion,
regardless of the type of reactant [1, 3]. The most stable olefin
that is possible is formed: this stability probably being due to
mesomeric hyperconjugation of the groups linked α and β about
the double bond, although other explanations have been offered
[130].

Some 20 years ago, Hughes and Ingold pointed out [131] that
such mesomeric stabilisation of the final products would be expected
to make an appearance as electromeric hyperconjugation in the
transition states of elimination and so to facilitate the path to the
most stable olefin. A carbanion-like transition state (type A) would
not evoke such stabilisation; but types B and C with either considerable double-bond character or possessing a developing p-
orbital on the α-carbon, would do so. Any suitable α- or β-linked
substituent would participate for structures of type B; and α-
substituents would do so for type C, and the effectiveness of the
contribution would depend on the capacity for hyperconjugation

with the unsaturation being developed or, more guardedly, on the capacity for olefin stabilisation, which is known to be the reverse of the inductive order, *i.e.*,

Me > Et > higher *prim*-alkyl > *i*-Pr > *t*-Bu

The possible transition states for a typical secondary structure are (XXa) and (XXb). Both the α- and β-linked methyl groups can stabilise double-bond formation in the left-hand branch to give the structure (a) much more efficiently than the α-bonded ethyl group can do so in the right-hand branch to give (b): hence the

(XXa)　　　　　　　　(XXb)

more alkylated product predominates and such considerations, applied to more general cases, always lead to Saytzeff-type orientation. The Saytzeff rule acts in the opposite direction to any statistical effect concerning the numbers of available β-hydrogens in the branches.

This theory has been tested in a manner similar to that for 'onium cases by measuring the elimination rates in straight-chain homologues and in each branch of secondary and tertiary compounds. Typical results for the former type are in Table 9 and the extensive

TABLE 9

RELATIVE E2 RATES FOR ALKYL HALIDES
R'R"CHCH$_2$Br + $\overline{\text{O}}$Et IN EtOH AT 55°

Alkyl group R'R"	Et H,H	n-Pr Me,H	n-Bu Et,H	n-Am n-Pr,H	i-Bu Me,Me	β-Phenylethyl Ph,H	α-Phenylethyl
Rel. rate	1.0	3.3	2.7	2.2	5.4	350	30

results available are discussed in Ingold's treatise *[1]*. These data are in complete accord with the predictions based on electromeric control and the last two entries in the table illustrate two other points: the first is that electromeric stabilisation occurs even more powerfully with aromatic substituents (or unsaturated substituents in general which possess double bonds or *p*-electrons) that are capable of exhibiting true conjugation, rather than hyperconjugation; and the other is that unlike the inductive effect, which is rapidly damped out by transmission across saturated atoms, the factors which influence Saytzeff orientation can act from both α- and β-positions to stabilise a developing double bond (but only from the α-position to stabilise a positive charge at the α-carbon in an E1-like transition state). When a conjugating group is substituted at the β-position, the elimination rate is always larger than when it is at the α: this is shown by the last two entries of Table 9, and also by the 200-fold more rapid rate of elimination of hydrogen bromide from $BrCH_2CH_2Br$ than from CH_3CHBr_2 *[132]*. Such results cannot be accounted for by electromeric stabilisation of transition states of either type C or B, and are due to the inductive effects of the substituents which can act from the β-position to loosen (in the cases just considered) the β-hydrogen which is to be lost, but have little effect when acting from the α-position. A methyl substituent would show a much weaker effect in the opposite direction. The predominance of the inductive effect for non-alkyl β-substituents was the reason why the deviations from the Hofmann rule of such substituted 'onium salts were interpreted (in the previous section) as being solely due to induction.

An unexpected situation arises when the relative rates (within a compound type) are compared for series of increasing conjugative capabilities (Table 10). The high value for the β-phenylethyl-ammonium salt is anomalous, but significant, and will be discussed in Chapter 4. The range of values for the 'onium series has been discussed previously, but the smaller effect of α-substituents in the bromides than in the sulphonium compounds might suggest that, although the former type did not obey the Hofmann rule, it possessed a transition state structure more nearly corresponding to

TABLE 10

RELATIVE RATES FOR INCREASING CONJUGATIVE ABILITY
IN E2 [1, 3, 34]

	Et	i-Pr	t-Bu	β-PhEt	α-PhEt
$R\overset{+}{S}Me_2$	1	70	200	430	100[*]
RBr	1	5	80	350	30[**]
$R\overset{+}{N}Me_3$	1	2	13	ca. 6,000	15[***]

[*] In EtOH,EtŌ at 64°.
[**] In EtOH,EtŌ at 55°.
[***] In EtOH,EtŌ at 104°.

type A than to the type B or C anticipated. However, type C
structures should be especially favoured for secondary and tertiary
bromides and it is possible that the stabilisation by the α-sub-
stituent in these cases is much less than is the corresponding
stabilisation of a developing double bond in the 'onium case, owing
to the flatter structure and greater possibility for orbital overlap
in the latter system. Even if complete C–Br heterolysis occurred
the configuration at C_α might not become planar, but could be held
nearly tetrahedral in the ion-pair (see Chap. 1, sect. 2b).

Kinetic studies of p-substituted 2-phenylethyl halides, tosylates,
and 'onium compounds under E2 conditions have been interpreted
[106, 133–134] on the basis of a structure of type A largely governed
by inductive effects, with the carbanionic character increasing in
this order. The detailed analysis was based on the Hammett
equation: the rate of elimination correlated with the inductive
power of the para-substituent as measured by its σ-value, and the
size of the ρ-value for each series indicated the magnitude of the
charge on the β-carbon in the transition state. There could have
been little double-bond character in these transition states, for the
p-methoxy compound which would have possessed the greatest
capacity for conjugation of any compound studied actually reacted
the slowest of all. This work is in agreement with the previously

mentioned conclusions concerning the dominance of inductive over conjugative tendencies in phenyl-substituted compounds, but obviously such conclusions cannot be extended to halides or tosylates not possessing this special structure: these latter compounds must favour the concerted or E1-like transition states. It is also possible that the β-phenylated halides and tosylates utilised a hybrid E1-E1cB-like transition state, as represented by (XXI), which is uniquely permitted in these series by the conjugative properties (both electromeric and mesomeric) of the β-substituent coupled with the ready fission of the α-linked group. In some cases, indeed, a correlation with σ^- rather than σ is found [134].

(XXI)

For a particular compound reacting under as similar conditions as possible, E1 reactions are found to obey the Saytzeff rule to a greater extent than E2 processes: thus for *tert.*-pentyl bromide [3];

$$t\text{-Pentyl Br} \Big\langle \begin{array}{l} \text{(E1)} \longrightarrow \text{2-pentene 82\% + 1-pentene 18\%} \\ \text{(E2)} \longrightarrow \text{2-pentene 71\% + 1-pentene 29\%} \end{array} \tag{40}$$

Presumedly this is because the conjugative stabilisation by α-substituents is more important in the nearly flat, carbonium-ion like transition state for the former reaction, than in the corresponding E2 case (especially in the E1-like type C, when the configuration at the α-carbon is almost tetrahedral: see discussion above). This state of affairs could not have been forecast, for the carbonium ion has an α-carbon with a formal positive charge which could well have stimulated inductive control*.

---

* The positive charge on the C_α-atom in a carbonium ion could be reduced both by inductive and hyperconjugative electron release from the rest of the structure. Only the former mode is readily available to reduce the charge on an 'onium atom.

Kinetically-controlled E1 studies have verified electromeric control in the same way as for E2 reactions [3]. The rate of ionisation of saturated structures, which seems to be mainly controlled by inductive factors, is not as significant for the mechanistic interpretation of these reactions as is the yield of olefin in the various alkyl branches which measures the relative case of the various product forming steps. Some typical examples of the latter are given:

$$(CH_3)_3CBr, \text{ EtOH at } 25° \quad \% \text{ olefin per Me group } 6.3$$
$$(CH_3)_2CEtBr, \text{ EtOH at } 25° \left\{ \begin{array}{l} \% \text{ olefin per Me group } 3.3 \\ \% \text{ olefin per Et group } 29.6 \end{array} \right.$$

Within the last few years certain workers [135–136] have implied that there is only one factor controlling orientation—the inductive effect—and that Saytzeff-type orientation is the result of subsequent isomerisation of the initially formed olefin in the presence of acid, which it is presumed is always formed. This view, although tenable for acid-catalysed dehydrations, is quite indefensible as a general proposition. No interconversion of olefins can take place in the base-catalysed E2 reactions of halides; and although such interconversions are conceivable in E1 reactions in which acid is generated, studies in which the reaction mixture was kept neutral by the addition of base as the reaction proceeded, or weakly alkaline by the addition of a weak base which did not promote E2 reactions, clearly show that the Saytzeff rule is still obeyed [3]. As the "Saytzeff"-olefin is the most stable of the possible isomers, it always predominates for eliminations carried out under equilibrating conditions. Thus the formation of this olefin in dehydrations catalysed by strong acids could be the result of thermodynamical control of the products, and no deductions concerning the mechanism can be drawn from product analyses.

3. The Co-existence of Orientating Effects

As should now be apparent, the inductive and electromeric effects are independent and are not mutually exclusive: both are always present, but one can be made to predominate by a change of the reactants which causes a change in the type of transition state of decomposition. Several examples of the intrusion of inductive effects on reactions which are controlled overall by electromeric influences, and *vice-versa*, have been given, and other instances are available [1, 3]. When one moves from the field of alkyl substituents to more polar groups, the effect which such changes will have on the transition state cannot always be easily predicted.

It should be possible to alter the structure of the transition state, through which a particular type of compound decomposes, from that typical of such compounds (in the commonly-used hydroxylic solvents) to types in which the opposite controlling influences predominate. This could be done by a suitable change of base and solvent, and a change of orientation would result. For instance, the E2 reactions of a tertiary sulphonium salt with ethoxide in ethanol obey Hofmann's rule, but if the transition state structure could be moved from the A-B type region to the B-C by changing to a weakly basic, poorly-solvating medium such as 2,6-dimethyl-pyridine, any E2 reaction that could be achieved should obey the Saytzeff rule. Such experiments have not been performed; but it has been shown [34] that primary 'onium compounds have a transition state for E2 which alters from type A towards type B as the solvent is changed from ethanol to *tert.*-butanol (and the base from ethoxide to *tert.*-butoxide), without however changing the overriding inductive control.

The effects of structural change, which have been interpreted here in terms of differences in transition state structures, have largely been correlated with rates: in few cases have the effects on individual Arrhenius parameters been studied. The inductive and electromeric effects would mainly affect the heat of activation. The entropy term would be dependent on the number of β-hydrogen atoms available and so on the probability of the correct orientation for trans-planar elimination, but this statistical effect can easily be allowed for when comparing the rates of a β-substituted series. A factor which could affect the entropy is the ponderal effect [137], which is a result of the distribution of mass in the transition state and has some importance in substitution; but theoretical estimations of this have not been carried out for elimination, and there is no necessity to introduce any such refinement to explain the present experimental data. Steric effects, which will now be discussed, could affect both heat and entropy terms, but it is found that such effects are unimportant except in special cases.

4. Steric Theories of Orientation

During the past 10 years, the theories described in the previous sections have been challenged several times by H. C. Brown, who postulates a more basic role for steric effects in this as in many other types of reactions*. Such effects are well-known for certain substitutions and ionisations, but it had been maintained that they would play a very minor role in eliminations except in complicated structures [3]. If secondary influences such as steric inhibition of resonance and solvation are neglected, three main types of steric effects can be visualised for elimination. (i) The β-hydrogens may be shielded from the attacking-base by a ramified alkyl structure. This is analogous to the effect occurring in neopentyl and other substitutions [13], but because of the more exposed positions of the atoms being attacked, it should be relatively less important in eliminations. Two probable examples occur for (XXII) and (XXIII): in the former case only the *exo*-olefin is formed [139], and in the latter no olefin at all, under conditions which should favour E2

(XXII)   (XXIII)

* The predominance of steric effects in eliminations had been suggested earlier [138], but the author had presented no experimental results to support his claim and had used an incorrect model of the transition state.

reactions *[140]*. (ii) Steric interference may occur between bulky groups coming *cis* across a developing double-bond: this is the effect mainly responsible for the difference in stability of *cis* and *trans* isomers and was considered in Chap. 1, sect. 2. (iii) The *trans*-planar configuration necessary to attain the transition state of lowest energy may not be achieved owing to bulk or electrostatic effects. Discussion of this point, especially concerning benzene hexachloride, was also made in Chap. 1, sect. 2. All these effects may occur in E2 reactions, and the first two in E1. Brown has interpreted some rate and product data for certain series of halides in terms of these effects, and then by a bold generalization has concluded that such influences control elimination rates in general.

(a) Steric effects in E1 reactions

The steric theory was first evoked in order to explain E1 rates and the Saytzeff rule *[141–142]*. The solvolysis of a series of tertiary halides was studied in which the bulk of the alkyl groups was progressively increased, and the effect on ionisation rate was considered as an indication of steric acceleration when strain between the bulky groups about the tetrahedral α-carbon atom in the initial state was released by the formation of a trigonal configuration in the carbonium ion. These effects were, however, small compared with the usual kinetic effects of steric hindrance and acceleration, and other workers have preferred a polar explanation *[143]*: in particular, one of a complex kind *[144]* in which the inductive effects of alkyl groups varied in an unusual manner as substituents were moved away from the reaction centre.

A steric explanation was also applied to the product-forming step. For moderate ramification the olefin yield was smaller than was expected on the basis of polar theory, and this was attributed to steric hindrance to proton abstraction. As the bulk of the substituents increased, the olefin yield became larger and this was supposedly because of steric hindrance to the substitution reaction, for any strain in the reactant molecule which was released by ionisation would be regenerated by subsequent addition to the carbonium ion, but not by elimination, eqn. (41). A "squeezing-out" of the proton was also believed to enhance the rate of elimination in bulky structures. The most complex structure which was studied

$$RX \longrightarrow R\overset{+}{\overset{}{X}}\overset{-}{} \text{ (less strain)} \xrightarrow{\;\overline{Y}\;} R\text{—}Y \text{ (strained)}$$
$$\text{(strained)} \qquad\quad \searrow \qquad\qquad\qquad\qquad (41)$$
$$\text{Olefin} + \overset{+}{H} \text{ (less strain)}$$

[142a] also showed Hofmann-type elimination, eqn. (42), instead of the Saytzeff-type which was expected, and found, with the simpler members of the homologous series, and this change in orientation was considered to be due to an eclipsing effect between the methyl and *tert.*-butyl groups in the transition state leading to the Saytzeff product.

$$(CH_3)_3CCH_2C(CH_3)_2Cl \xrightarrow{\;E1\;} \begin{cases} (CH_3)_3CCH_2C(CH_3):CH_2 & (81\%) \\ (CH_3)_3CCH:C(CH_3)_2 & (19\%) \end{cases} \qquad (42)$$
$$(XXIV)$$

Later workers have shown *[145]* that the polar theory had been incorrectly applied in making the predictions of the olefin yields from these compounds: in particular the ability of substituents situated at either end of a developing double-bond to show electromeric effects had been neglected. If this was allowed for, most of the olefin yields could be interpreted on the basis of electromeric control, and a semi-quantitative method of calculation, based on polar theory, was developed by which the total olefin yields and isomer ratios could be calculated to within a few percentage units of the experimental values for nine of the twelve cases considered by Brown (and also for most of the other available data for the E1 and E2 reactions of halides). Poor agreement was obtained for the three most ramified cases (XXIV)–(XXVI): however, the intervention of rearrangement-type forces in these structures could not be ruled out, and the important discovery was made that the Saytzeff rule was violated for (XXIV) because the rate of elimination in the methyl branches was facilitated compared with the rate in such branches of lower homologues:

$$(CH_3)_3C\cdot C(CH_3)_2Cl \qquad\qquad (CH_3)_3C\cdot C(C_2H_5)_2Cl$$
$$(XXV) \qquad\qquad\qquad\qquad (XXVI)$$

in particular the rate of elimination in the neopentyl branch was not retarded, but was "normal" as compared with the rates in simpler compounds. This was quite contrary to the steric theory, which would require the orientation to arise from a "normal" rate in the methyl branches but a retarded rate in the neopentyl branch. This phenomenon, together with the abnormally large rate of solvolysis and the high olefin yield, was attributed to the occurrence of *tert.*-butyl group hyperconjugation in the ionisation and product steps as shown in eqns. (43) and (44) and other evidence was

$$(CH_3)_3C-CH_2-CMe_2-Cl \longrightarrow (CH_3)_3C-CH_2-\overset{+}{C}Me_2\bar{C}l \qquad (43)$$

$$(CH_3)_3C-CH_2-\overset{\delta+}{C}\cdots CH_2\cdots\overset{\delta+}{H} \longrightarrow (CH_3)_3C-CH_2-C=CH_2 +\overset{+}{H} \qquad (44)$$
$$\underset{CH_3}{|} \qquad\qquad\qquad\qquad \underset{CH_3}{|}$$

presented for this unusual mode of electron release. This explanation has been challenged [142d], but the demonstration that rearrangement does not occur in these structures, and the conclusion that therefore rearrangement-type forces can have no influence, is irrelevant, for such reasoning would deny the kinetic effects of hydrogen hyperconjugation unless the atoms involved were split-off as protons.

Without detailed kinetic investigations it is difficult to establish whether the irregularities observed in the other structures indicate steric (non-bonding) interactions or whether they arise from bonding interactions of the kind which at greater intensities can cause fragmentations or rearrangements. They are certainly not unambiguous evidence for the suggested generalisation of steric control.

The danger of such generalisations is evident when the experimental data are considered in terms of the transition states that are involved. The Saytzeff-type olefin from (XXIV) is about 1.5 kcal.mole^{-1} less stable than the Hofmann product (as has been determined from measurements of heats of hydrogenation) [146], and this is reasonably attributed to *cis*-effects between the α- and

β-substituents. The steric theory requires these effects to be dominant in the transition state leading to the products; but the kinetic data clearly indicate that this is not so, and that the transition state probably resembles a carbonium ion in which such steric interactions can be calculated to be negligible. This is as far as we can go from the experimental data. A rationalisation of the factors stabilising a "carbonium-ion-like" rather than an "olefin-like" transition state involves such vexed topics as the nature of steric and hyperconjugative effects [130], the difference between C–C and C–H hyperconjugation [147], the stereochemical requirements for C–H hyperconjugation [148] and the reaction conditions, but it is not safe to extend any conclusions to homologues of the same type and certainly not to other types of compounds, for the structure of the transition state may well be different, either in detail or in extent, from that of the one more fully analysed. The orientation rules are manifestations of transition state-structures, and are not universal properties of a particular reaction-type.

(b) Steric effects in E2 reactions

Steric hindrance can influence some E2 reactions and two examples have already been cited. Also the geometry of the base is sometimes significant, for one optical isomer of α-benzene hexachloride [149] or potentially resolvable bromoalkanes [86a, 150] can be destroyed in preference to the other by a ramified optically-active base such as brucine in an elimination process, and so an optically active mixture can result if insufficient base is used to destroy all the substrate.

Recently, Brown has applied his general steric theory to E2 reactions [151]. Now, contrary to the arguments which were summarised in the preceding section (a), the electromeric effect is allowed to control the Saytzeff pattern of structural effects, but steric strain is to replace the inductive effect as the cause of the Hofmann pattern. He makes it clear that a steric effect of limited incidence is not visualised, but one is claimed which is in universal control down to the simplest alkyl groups: the substitution of steric strain for the inductive effect is to be total.

The steric theory may be summarised in terms of the two transition states (XXVII) and (XXVIII) available for an eliminating molecule RCH_2CHXCH_3. The former leads to Saytzeff-type elimination and is favoured by electromeric influences, but this structure is more

(XXVII)   (XXVIII)

affected by steric strain between B, R, and X than in the alternative structure which leads to the Hofmann product. Accordingly, as the bulk of these three groups increases, a change to the latter type of orientation will be favoured, and this should be accompanied by a decrease in rate. When X is bulky, as in 'onium compounds, structure (XXVIII) is always preferred, for steric effects always outweigh electromeric effects in controlling the relative stabilities. In El reactions most of the strain is removed on ionisation, and so here the electromeric effect would have maximum influence. Inductive effects were considered negligible for both mechanisms.

In support of this view three sets of data, almost entirely of a product-isolation kind, were put forward, which were claimed to demonstrate the three types of steric effect listed at the start of this section. The first set [151a] contained analyses of the olefin mixtures from the decomposition of RCH_2CMe_2Br with ethoxide, where R was Me, Et, i-Pr and t-Bu. A "steady transition" from Saytzeff to Hofmann control was claimed as this series was traversed due to an increase in the steric requirements of the alkyl groups which came cis across a developing double-bond, and also to strain between the leaving group and the β-linked alkyl groups in the trans-planar transition state leading to the Saytzeff product. A more detailed analysis [34], which took into consideration the number of available β-hydrogen atoms in each case, indicated

that the Saytzeff rule was strongly obeyed in the first three examples: the large discontinuity occurred with the last, where, as
for the analogous E1 case, either steric or non-bonded interactions
were possible. It was not recorded whether the changed orientation
was associated with an increased or a decreased rate.

The second argument related to variations in the attacking-
base [151b,c]. Several substrates and ramified bases were used,
and it was found that as the bulk of the base was increased in the
order $\overline{O}Et$, $\overline{O}Bu^t$, $\overline{O}CEt_3$ (using the respective alcohols as solvents)
the orientation changed from Saytzeff-like to Hofmann-like. A
typical example was for $(CH_3)_2CHCMe_2Br$ for which the per-
centages of the 1-olefin (Hofmann product) with the above bases
were 21, 73, and 92% respectively. This work is very important
from a preparative viewpoint but it is difficult to assess it mecha-
nistically. The change in the base and solvent would cause differences other than mere bulk effects, for poorer solvating media
will discourage C–Br breakage and the associated stronger base
should increasingly promote C–H breakage in the transition state;
all this reducing its saturation and diminishing the predominance
of the Saytzeff pattern of influences [34]. Even if the diametrically
extreme view was held that such changes caused more unsaturation,
eclipsing effects might occur in the Saytzeff-type transition state
which were quite atypical for the solvents and conditions usually
associated with the Saytzeff rule. On either count, the reaction
conditions are so unusual that any generalisation of the results
obtained therein to the more familiar conditions is unjustified.

The third argument [151d] concerned variations in the α-leaving
group, which in reactions of 2-pentyl compounds with ethoxide
ions affected olefin composition as follows:

X in $CH_3CH_2CH_2CHXCH_3$	Br	I	OTs	SO_2Me	$\overset{+}{S}Me_2$	$\overset{+}{N}Me_3$
alk-1-ene %	31	30	48	89	87	98

From halides to 'onium compounds, the orientation changed, as
is usual, from Saytzeff-type to Hofmann-type. The proposal was
that the larger steric requirements of the 'onium groups were

responsible. However, the alternative still seems open that the responsible factor was their charge, or more accurately their electronegativity.

None of this evidence is thus conclusive for the deductions drawn and recently much evidence for the general unimportance of steric hindrance has been collected. Before the steric theory had been published, it had been concluded [152] from accurate mass-spectrometric analyses of the olefin mixtures from compounds $R_1R_2R_3R_4\overset{+}{N}\overline{O}H$ that inductive control of elimination was predominant, except possibly for the most complex alkyl substituents such as neohexyl $(CH_3)_3C \cdot CH_2CH_2$ and isopentyl $(CH_3)_2CH \cdot CH_2CH_2$, when steric hindrance might occur. Another important observation [153] was that nitro compounds, like sulphones, obey the Hofmann rule. Both of these groups contain formally positive atoms bonded to the α-carbon and on the basis of inductive control they would be expected to behave analogously; but on the basis of the steric theory the nitro group should obey the Saytzeff rule, for it is smaller than an iodine substituent (which, of course does so). The indifference of quite ramified systems to the degree of bulk and branching of the attacking base has been noted [29, 34, 86], and also the unimportance of the bulk of the leaving group in alkyl halides [154]. This latter point must be interpreted with some caution, for N.M.R. studies have shown that the steric effects of halogen atoms are due to a combination of bulk and polarisability factors and can fall in an order unexpected from the Van der Waals radii [464].

Evidence supporting inductive control has also been obtained from a correlation of the rates of elimination from *para*-substituted 2-phenylethylsulphonium compounds with the Hammett-σ-(inductive)-constant of the substituent [133, 134]. The extension to simpler alkyl systems is rather uncertain, but it was argued that inductive effects would still here be in control. The position of steric theory as applied to compounds with non-alkyl substituents of high inductive power is not clear; for it has never been stated whether such powerful polar groups could outweigh the supposed steric influences in governing the direction of reaction. In practice, inductive effects are found to predominate for β-halogenated bromoalkanes and conjugative and steric effects are not important [155]. This is in accord with conclusions concerning earlier studies [2] which can only be satisfactorily interpreted on the basis of inductive control (see sect. 1). Support for the steric theory has been claimed from results on the orientation of olefin formation from amine-oxides (R_1R_2MeNO) [52]. These reactions involve a cyclic transition state (see Chapter 7) and the quantities of the two olefins were approximately proportional to the numbers of β-hydrogens available ;neither Hofmann- nor Saytzeff-like orientation being apparent. Steric effects were not expected in transition states of this geometry, and as effects of polarity and unsaturation cancelled, it was assumed that both were individually small. The further conclusion that polarity is also insignificant in E2 'onium decompositions and that accordingly these owe their Hofmann-type orientation to steric effects is obviously inconsequential and is an example of the tendency, which is so prevalent in mechanistic discussions, of arguing from one particular compound-type to general conclusions. Another example of this tendency, applied to the inductive-steric controversy, has recently appeared [465].

A main tenet of the steric theory is a denial of the ability of an 'onium atom to induce a sufficiently large positive charge at a site several atoms removed to account for the observed orientation. The charge on a nitrogen or sulphur 'onium atom is certainly not the formal unit which is conventionally assigned, but the dipole moments of sulphones and amine-oxides indicate that it is probably at least half a positive electronic charge, and such a potential would be expected to possess considerable polarising power. This effect can operate at a distance of several carbon atoms as is shown by the orientation of the addition of water to acetylenes [156] and by the effects of trimethylammonium substituents on the dissociation constants of acids. Examples of the latter are shown in the order of pK_{a_+} values 4.80, 1.83 and 4.27 for CH_3COOH, $\overset{+}{N}Me_3CH_2COOH$ and $\overset{+}{N}Me_3(CH_2)_4COOH$, where the large labilising effect of a formal positive charge on a hydrogen atom which is 4 atoms removed is illustrated by the second value; and the damping effect of a chain

of carbon atoms (or increase in direct distance) by the last. Refine-
ments in the theory and practice of nuclear-magnetic-resonance
spectroscopy may make the charge density on such labile hydrogen
atoms directly measurable.

As previously mentioned (see sect. 1), theoretical calculations
have shown that the charge densities induced on the β-hydrogen
atoms are sufficient to account for the differences in free energy
of activation which are observed, if the assumption (which is
surely reasonable within a homologous series) is made that such
differences are entirely due to the differences in acidity of the
substrate. These calculations also show that the inductive effect
is damped by a factor of about five-fold on passing through a
saturated atom, rather than the factor of three which has been
suggested on the basis of the variation on the acid dissociation
constant with homology [34]. This difference is understandable, for
the method of calculation assumes propagation of the inductive
effect through the bonds, and hence exponential attenuation,
whereas part must be due to the direct effect, with power-law
attenuation: thus in practice a slower fading would be achieved
than would be predicted by this theoretical treatment.

Recently a kinetic study [34, 157] of the E2 reactions of 'onium
compounds has provided more evidence for inductive control. The
decomposition of $R_1RCHCH_2-\overset{+}{N}Me_3$ and $-\overset{+}{S}Me_2$ by ethoxide and
tert.-butoxide ion in the corresponding alcohols as solvents was
studied with R_1 increasing in homology from hydrogen to tert.-butyl
and with R being methyl or hydrogen. Polar control would show
a smoothly decreasing elimination rate as the homology of the
β-substituent was increased, but steric hindrance would be characterised by a sudden rapid decrease, once a certain threshold of
material density was exceeded. The pattern of results for the series
(part of which is included in Tables 8 and 10), and its variation
with solvent, base, and substrate structure, could only be plausibly
interpreted by the inductive theory. A linear free-energy relationship based on inductive control was obeyed in all cases except for
the neohexyl compounds ($t-BuCH_2CH_2X$) for which the rate was
usually considerably smaller than was expected, and this latter

occurrence was interpreted as due to an inability of these compounds to attain a trans-planar transition state of type A owing to the interference between the bulky β-substituent and the α-linked leaving group. Calculations showed that an angular distortion of some 20–30° (diagram (VII), Chap. 1, sect. 2) occurred, and this increased the free energy of activation by about 1.5–2.2 kcal.mole^{-1}. For the neohexylsulphonium salt in *tert.*-butanol this retarding effect did not occur and the rate was as predicted on inductive theory: presumably a transition state of type B was now employed, which is especially favoured for sulphonium salts under these conditions, and the flatter structure removed any restrictions to the attainment of planarity. The presence of an α-phenyl substituent, which should also favour a tendency for flatter transition states, also removed the steric effects in both ethanol and *tert.*-butanol. In none of this work was any steric effect distinguishable due to the bulk of the base, and calculations confirmed the absence of this. An opposite view has been put forward on the basis of a different semi-quantitative method of calculation [158]. A complementary kinetic investigation of compounds $(CH_3)_3CCH\overset{+}{N}Me_3CHRR^1$ where R and R^1 were hydrogens or methyl groups showed that no eclipsing effects occurred even when methyl and *tert.*-butyl groups were coming *cis* across the double bond; nor did any frontal effects appear between the *tert.*-butyl group and the attacking base [34]. This indicates that the transition states resembled the initial states (Type A), as is expected for 'onium compounds. Calculations and models showed that no steric effects would appear for such configurations, but large ones could be present in a flattened, concerted transition state as would probably occur for halides.

Once a large body of kinetic data had been obtained, the rate factors for elimination in particular alkyl groups could be applied to the elimination in the branches of complex 'onium compounds and so the proportion of the isomers calculated. In nearly all cases an excellent agreement with experiment was obtained [34], and elimination thus occurred in each branch at a rate independent of the presence of other branches, but proportional to the rates in the alkyl groups of simple compounds of the types $R\overset{+}{N}Me_3$ and $R\overset{+}{S}Me_2$.

In particular, steric interactions involving substituents on the 'onium atoms were negligible.

The conclusion from this work is that inductive control is predominant for most alkyl systems; steric hindrance only entering as a complication above certain determinable thresholds of structural complexity, as would be expected from its short-range nature. Arguments by analogy concerning such effects from one compound type to another are valueless.

Besides the strong forces of electropolarity and unsaturation, and the occasional strong forces of steric repulsion, there must exist between the parts of any reacting system, weaker, but longer-range, and hence more or less general forces, of which it seems very difficult to take account, such as quadrupole and various forms of electron-correlation forces. Intervalency forces exist in ethane which have nothing to do with group interpenetration as determined from Van der Waals radii, but are responsible for the restrictions to free rotation, and these must be general to alkyl structures [159]. Such forces should cause energy effects when rotation of a β-linked substituent takes place from a position *trans* to the leaving group (XXIX), as usually is the ground-state conformation, to the *cis*-position required to enter the transition state (XXX). It is difficult

(XXIX)   (XXX)

to estimate the magnitude of these effects, as little data concerning the conformational equilibria of 'onium compounds and halides are available, but they are probably small; or if not, they appear to be constant for a homologous series and so produce no noticable consequences [79].

Chapter 4

LESS USUAL ELIMINATION MECHANISMS

Several mechanisms for elimination besides E1 and E2 have been suggested, together with varying amounts of supporting evidence. Although uncommon, they are of interest as illustrations of the modifications which the usual schemes can undergo in atypical structures and environments.

1. E1cB Mechanisms

A mechanism has already been briefly mentioned (Chap. 1, sect. 1b) in which the C_β–H bond is broken in the first step of a two-stage process, eqn. (45). It was originally assumed that step —1 was

$$B + CHR_2CR_2X \; \underset{-1}{\overset{1}{\rightleftharpoons}} \; B\overset{+}{H} + \bar{C}R_2CR_2X \tag{45}$$

$$\bar{C}R_2CR_2X \; \overset{2}{\longrightarrow} \; CR_2:CR_2 + \bar{X}$$

much faster than 2, and so the first stage of this process—the formation of the carbanion from the substrate—was in equilibrium. This special case obeys the rate equation (46), and when the base is the lyate ion of the solvent, as almost invariably happens, this reduces to simple second order kinetics.

$$\text{Rate} = k_2 k_1 \, [\text{B}] \, [\text{S}]/k_{-1} \, [\overset{+}{\text{B}}\text{H}] \tag{46}$$

Variants of this mechanism can occur in which the carbanion can decompose to form olefin at a rate comparable to or greater than that at which it can revert to the original molecule and here the equilibrium condition does not apply. In the limiting case when every carbanion passes into elimination products, the mechanism will degenerate into an E2 process involving an E1cB-like transition state, but a whole spectrum of cases may exist between the two-stage equilibrium and the one-step concerted process for which a reaction intermediate of varying stability is formed. This is best appreciated by consideration of the free energy diagram (XXXI),

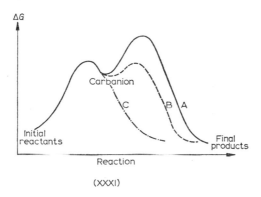

(XXXI)

in which curve A represents the situation for a two-stage process, the first stage of which is at equilibrium; curve B the case when equilibrium is not achieved; and curve C the concerted E2 mechanism. Especially reactive carbanions may have a greater tendency to form olefins than to reform their parent molecule, for the reverse of step 1 may be entirely governed by an unfavourable entropy term connected with the necessity for special orientation of the solvent about the carbanion, such as occurs in the neutralisation of carbonium ions [15]. In other words, an increase in the reactivity of the carbanionic intermediate may affect k_2 rather than k_{-1}.

As a carbanion is very reactive, the steady-state hypothesis can be applied to its concentration and a rate expression (47) is obtained for the general E1cB case, which again reduces to a second-order

$$\text{Rate} = k_1 k_2 [\text{B}] [\text{S}]/k_{-1} [\overset{+}{\text{BH}}] + k_2 \qquad (47)$$

form when the base is the lyate ion. When $k_2 \gg k_{-1} [\overset{+}{\text{BH}}]$, the equation for the E2 mechanism is obtained, and when $k_{-1} [\overset{+}{\text{BH}}] \gg$

k_2, the equation becomes identical with eqn. (46)—the equilibrium case.

Although many olefin-eliminations obey second-order kinetics, there is no reason to believe that more than a few special structures undergo the two-stage process. An estimate can be made of the activation energies required for one- and two-stage mechanisms for any particular compound by use of the rule that such quantities are usually about 1/4 to 1/2 of the heats of reaction (which can also be estimated for each mechanism), and the former process is always found [31b] to be favoured by some 7–14 kcal.mole^{-1}. Rate and stereochemical patterns for second-order eliminations also can be best interpreted on the basis of a one-step mechanism.

Studies using isotopic tracers are among the best means for the delineation of the scope of two-step mechanisms, and two good examples are the bimolecular decompositions of β-phenylethyl bromide with ethoxide ion in deuterium ethoxide (EtOD), and of Et_2CDCH_2Br with sodamide in liquid ammonia [160]. If two-step processes were easily accessible, these are two situations which would surely exhibit them; for the former involves a β-linked phenyl group which can both facilitate β-hydrogen loss and stabilise the resultant carbanion, and the latter takes place under exceptionally basic conditions where proton-abstraction might well occur without any energetic assistance from double-bond formation. When either of these reactions was stopped at about half completion, the unreacted substrate was found to be completely free (within the limits of the analytical method) of deuterium in the former example and of β-linked protium in the latter. Either an equilibrium or considerable reversibility in the first stage would result in isotope exchange with the solvent, for the carbanions should be rapidly neutralised by the solvation shell, and so these results imply that either a one-stage mechanism is followed or a two-stage mechanism occurs in which the carbanion is exceptionally unstable with respect to elimination and so $k_2 \gg k_{-1}$. In view of the calculations previously mentioned and the general evidence for concerted processes, the former alternative is definitely to be preferred.

Interesting results are obtained for β-benzene hexachloride, which cannot easily undergo normal E2 reactions because of stereochemical restrictions (*cf.* Chap. 1, sect. 2a) but which will decompose under certain conditions either by a two-stage process or by a one-stage *cis*- or *trans*-elimination that is forced against the normal geometrical requirements. When the reaction was carried out in a solvent containing deuterium [161], only small amounts of tracer were picked up by the unreacted substrate, and this was interpreted on the basis of a non-equilibrium process, (48) in which only one carbanion reverted to the initial reactant for every 150 which

$$(48)$$

Products

passed on to products: the inversion of the carbanion in the second step was presumed to be very rapid, for such species were believed to be completely optically unstable in these conditions. The activation energy was in excess of the value for the unrestricted isomers by about 12 kcal.mole^{-1} and this falls in the range of the calculated excess for two-stage reactions. Other workers have questioned this interpretation [32], and have preferred one of the types of forced mechanisms.

A reaction of low activation energy, such as the decomposition of a carbanion, may not exhibit the usual *trans*-planar specificity for elimination*, and so the lone pair of electrons on the β-carbon might eject the leaving group without the necessity for an inversion into the *anti*-position with respect to it, as in the last step of eqn. (48). Proton abstraction to form a carbanion could occur from any conformation of the substrate, and a *cis*-ejection of the leaving group, coupled with the possibility of inversion and loss of configuration at the β-carbon, could lead to either *cis* or *trans* overall

---

* For amplification of this, see p. 25 and p. 160.

elimination. A definite rule for the orientation cannot be given for E1cB reactions: each case must be considered separately from the viewpoint of the size and type of substituents and the stability of the carbanion.

E1cB mechanisms are favoured by the same changes of structure and environment that favour the E2 process with an E1cB-like transition state (Chap. 1, sect. 3d) and the characteristic features of the mechanism are also similar to those exhibited by this, their limiting case. The equilibrium and non-equilibrium cases do differ in some aspects, however, besides the ability to come into isotopic equilibrium with the medium. The β-deuterium isotope effect will depend on the stability of the carbanion, for if a pre-equilibrium occurs $(k_{-1} \gg k_2)$ all β-linked tracer will be replaced by protium from the solvent before the reaction has appreciably started, and so no kinetic isotope effect will result; but as k_{-1} and k_2 become comparable, an increasing isotope effect will occur and near the limiting case, when $k_2 > k_{-1}$, the full isotope effect for the particular reaction would be exhibited. The alternative experimental technique would be to study the isotopically-normal substrate in a completely deuterated solvent; then an equilibrium case would show the maximum isotope effect that can be observed for the particular reaction, and the non-equilibrium cases would show lower effects which fall to unity as k_2 becomes greater than k_{-1}.

Another kinetic distinction between the extremes of the E1cB mechanism is that the equilibrium type is specifically catalysed by the lyate ion of the solvent [162], whereas a process in which the first step is far removed from equilibrium is catalysed by bases in general, as is the normal E2. This follows from a consideration of the solution equilibria in each case. As there is no sharp division between the equilibrium and non-equilibrium processes, there can be no sharp application of this criterion; but the fact of general base catalysis (which is often observed, see later) does enable an estimate to be made, from a knowledge of the equilibrium and rate constants which appear in the rate expression, of an upper limit to the half-life of any anionic intermediate. Specific catalysis has never been observed, but it would not be a decisive criterion for mechanism, since any reaction which in theory should show general base catalysis, would in practice show specific catalysis if the Brønsted exponent for the lyate ion were large, *i.e.*, if the catalytic efficiency of the lyate ion was much greater than that of the other available bases.

The prediction of the effects of substituents on the rates of ElcB processes is difficult, because the observed rate constants are composite, and the effect on each individual step must be weighted. As step 1 is highly endothermic, its transition state should resemble a carbanion in electronic structure, and similarly the exothermic step 2 should also have a structure much more resembling this intermediate than the final olefinic products. Unsaturation is thus almost absent in these structures and electron-releasing electromeric properties of substituents should be unimportant: electromeric electron-attracting β-substituents should however remove negative charge from the carbanion by initiating double-bond formation involving overlap of p- or d-orbitals with the lone-pair on the β-carbon, and so stabilise the ion. Inductive effects of β-groups should also be important: such electron-release should retard the first step, but facilitate the reverse and final steps. Only if $k_2 \gg k_{-1} [\overset{+}{B}H]$, which is not in general true, will the measured rate-constant be governed by the polar effects on the first step, but if the effects of alkyl substituents on k_2 and k_{-1} approximately cancel, then the inductive effect on this first step will predominate, and the Hofmann pattern of rates will be followed, even for halides.

Unfortunately, only fragmentary data are available for interpretation in the light of these several criteria between the one- and two-step processes, and between the variants of the latter, but it does seem that the ElcB mechanisms will only occur for specially activated structures or where there are stereochemical restrictions to the normal E2 process; at least for olefin forming reactions. Some examples will be considered shortly.

Many reactions involving compounds with labile hydrogens, but which do not form olefins, must proceed through equilibrium-type ElcB reactions. Examples are the reverse of carbonyl additions, scheme (49) and similar decompositions of structures $H\!-\!\overset{|}{N}\!-\!\overset{|}{\underset{|}{C}}\!-\!Y$ and $H\!-\!S\!-\!\overset{|}{\underset{|}{C}}\!-\!Y$.

$$H\!-\!O\!-\!\overset{|}{\underset{|}{C}}\!-\!Y \overset{B,}{\underset{-1}{\rightleftharpoons}} \overset{-}{O}\!\cdot\!\overset{|}{\underset{|}{C}}\!\cdot\!\overset{\frown}{Y} \overset{2}{\longrightarrow} O\!=\!\overset{|}{C} + \bar{Y} \qquad (49)$$

$$(k_1 \geqslant k_{-1} > k_2)$$

Y = ·CN	Cyanohydrin hydrolysis
·CH$_2$COCH$_3$	Depolymerisation of diketone alcohols
·CH$_2$CHO	Reverse aldol condensation
·OH	Dehydration of aldehyde hydrates
·OR	Hemi-acetal hydrolysis

Another excellent series of examples, albeit for α-elimination in non-olefin-forming reactions, is the hydrolysis of haloforms, for which a scheme (50) has been suggested in which the initial proton-transfer is slow [163a]. Sometimes k_2 is found to be [163d]

$$CHX_3 \underset{-1}{\overset{OH^-}{\rightleftharpoons}} \bar{C}X_3 \overset{}{\underset{2}{\longrightarrow}} :CX_2 + \bar{X} \overset{3}{\longrightarrow} \text{Products}$$

$$(k_{-1} > k_2; \; k_3 \text{ is very large})$$

(50)

of the same magnitude as k_{-1}. Evidence for this mechanism was the necessity for strongly basic reagents, the rate pattern, the identification of the carbene intermediate by trapping procedures, and the exchange of tracer with the solvent by deuterated substrates. A small isotope effect of about 1.3 was found in some cases for the initial proton removal from carbon [163b–d], and this is consistent with the highly endo-energetic nature of a carbanion-forming step. It is presumably the labilising influence of the halogen substituents which enables the mechanism to operate in this and related cases [164], and the trifluoromethyl group in CF_3CHX_2 can act similarly and probably leads to the formation of an olefin, which, however, is unstable under the reaction conditions [163c]. Some results [155] for bimolecular elimination from XCH_2CH_2Br (X = halogen), in which the removal of HBr was facilitated in an order $Br > Cl > F$ which was difficult to interpret convincingly on either steric or polar theories, might be similarly explained on the basis of a two-step mechanism: carbanion stabilisation would be favoured in this sequence, but the labilising influence on β-hydrogens should be the reverse.

Many other α-eliminations undoubtedly involve similar pathways, but quantitative studies are lacking. ElcB processes have probably been achieved in several olefin-forming reactions, mostly under non-kinetic conditions, but full diagnostic tests (such as are available) have not yet been carried out. An early example [165] was the alkaline decomposition of compounds $\overline{S}O_3CH_2CH_2X$ (X = halogen), in which the sulphonate group (despite its formal negative charge) is electron-attracting as is shown by its directive influence in aromatic substitution and its effect on the dissociation constants of acids. Another favourable structure occurs in $CDCl_2CDCl_2$, which was shown to form $CDCl:CCl_2$ on reaction with base with 10–15% exchange of deuterium for protium from the solvent [166], and a similar mechanism may occur in the loss of a hydrogen α to a trichloromethyl group in $Cl_3C(CH_2)_nCH_2Cl$ and related compounds [167]. Qualitative information indicates that other groups can influence the reactivity in a way that can be interpreted on the basis of two-step processes [168–171], and specific examples are the ready tendency of $NO_2CH_2CH_2NR_2$, $RCH(OAc)CH_2NO_2$, and $RCH(OAc)CHRCOEt$ (R = alkyl) to form olefins [102b, 172], and the facile decompositions of $RCOCH_2CH_2\overset{+}{S}Me_2\overline{O}H$ and $PhSO_2CH_2CH_2\overset{+}{S}Me_2\overline{O}H$ in aqueous solution at room temperature under conditions much milder than usual for 'onium decompositions [173]. In the last case the presence of the electron-attracting sulphonium group should encourage proton loss, and the powerfully electron-attracting phenylsulphone substituent should favour carbanion formation by both loosening the β-hydrogen and stabilising the negative charge on the β-carbon atom by d-orbital resonance [466, 467]. Compounds containing such a β-substituent might seem the most favourable for utilising the ElcB mechanism, but the collaboration of a powerful -I group at the α-carbon may be necessary to achieve this, for in strongly basic conditions the diastereoisomers of $PhSO_2CHCH_3CHCH_3I$ show completely stereospecific *trans*-elimination [174], and hence probably react by a E2 mechanism*. Some recent qualitative observations [175] concerning deuterium uptake into compounds $NO_2C_6H_4CH_2CH_2SCH_2COOH$ indicate at least a partially reversible first step. The compounds $(p\text{-}RC_6H_4)_2CHCCl_3$ would appear potentially favourable for E1cB, but kinetic and isotope effects are in accord with a concerted E2 process [176].

An especially likely case for E1cB should be $p\text{-}NO_2C_6H_4CH_2CH_2\text{-}\overset{+}{N}Me_3\bar{I}$. As long ago as 1933 [177], this was found to decompose readily in water at 100°, whereas other 'onium salts required the presence of hydroxide ion at higher temperatures, and the rate was found to be accelerated by alkali but depressed by added acid. This was interpreted at first as a two-step process with the solvent acting as the base to remove the exceptionally labile hydrogen, while the effect of the acid was to reverse the initial equilibrium. Later it was concluded that the process was E2, although on this explanation the only function of the acid would be to reduce the hydroxide ion concentration due to autoprotolysis of the solvent [163c], and this hydroxide would surely be negligible compared with the base capacity of the overwhelmingly greater concentration of solvent molecules. The β-tritium isotope effect was about 7 (theoretical maximum *ca.* 16) and was also held to support this mechanism [179], although it could also be consistent with an E1cB process**. This compound is currently being investigated [60], for it has all the desirable properties for an E1cB mode of decomposition—a β-substituent with exceptionally strong proton-loosening and anion stabilising powers and an α-bonded group which can activate a β-hydrogen—and reaction occurs in a strongly solvating medium which ensures that the $C\text{-}\overset{+}{N}$ bond is not easily broken. More highly substituted compounds such as 2,4,6-trinitro-2-phenylethyl 'onium salts should show a still greater tendency to pursue two-step mechanisms, and certainly these are found to

---

* For a qualification of this statement, see p. 94.
** Some difficulties in the interpretations of tritium-isotope studies of this sort have recently been pointed out [180].

be extremely unstable in very dilute alkali or aqueous solutions, even at room temperature [181, 182].

Other highly probable 2 step processes are the thermal elimination of H_2O, HX and NHR_2 from aldols, $RCHOHCH_2CHO$ [178], Michael adducts R_2CXCH_2COR [178, 185], and Mannich bases $RCOCH_2CH_2NR_2$ [183] respectively. All these types have very activated β-hydrogens.

A possible kinetic criterion for ElcB reactions of the equilibrium type is that the rates of such processes should be proportional to a basicity function h_- (see Chap. 2, sect. 1), rather than to the stoichiometric base concentration; and it was adduced [59] that the known ElcB decomposition of chloroform had a constant order in h_- of 0.8 but a rapidly increasing order in methoxide as the base concentration was increased up to 2 M sodium methoxide in methanol, which is the only system for which an h_- function has been defined. On the other hand, the known E2 decompositions of β-phenylethyl chloride had an order in methoxide of approx. 1.0 over the same range. Recent work [60] shows that such a criterion is not clear-cut, for at higher base concentrations of up to 4 M, the order in methoxide for the β-phenylethyl example increased sharply above 1. However, it seems significant that the rate of elimination from β-phenylethyltrimethylammonium ion correlated with h_- in a manner closely resembling that of the chloroform decomposition; for this substrate is well endowed for ElcB processes and as shown in Table 10 (p. 62) has an anomalous rate compared with other 'onium salts, which suggests a difference of mechanism. or of transition-state type.

A good test of this theory would be a study of the base catalysed decomposition of the difluorohalomethanes $CHXF_2$, for alone of the haloforms which have been studied these did not exchange deuterium with the solvent during reaction and so either pursued a synchronous E2 or an ElcB process of the extreme non-equilibrium type [184]. Apparently the powerful inductive effect of the fluorine is not sufficient to permit carbanion formation in the absence of overlap of low-energy d-orbitals.

An increase in base strength could also facilitate ElcB processes for suitable structures, and a significant observation is that although elimination from the diastereo-isomers $PhCHCH_3CHCH_3\overset{+}{N}Me_3\bar{X}$ with ethoxide in ethanol gave only *trans*-elimination, *cis*-elimination occurred with *tert.*-butoxide in *tert.*-butanol in at least one case, for both isomers gave the same olefin [29]. Here the combination of 'onium group and strong base should be offset somewhat by the poorly solvating medium which should favour $C_\alpha-\overset{+}{N}$ breakage, but an E1cB mechanism or at least an E2 mechanism with an E1cB-like transition state may be occurring. Base strength falls in the order (51). The first four anions can only exist in aprotic

$$n\text{-}\bar{Bu} > \bar{Ph} > \bar{Me} > Ph_3\bar{C} > \bar{NH}_2 > \bar{OR} > \bar{OH} \tag{51}$$

conditions and amide ion in liquid ammonia also, and it is in these conditions that 2-step processes may well occur. Little concrete evidence is available, but one example is the formation of "benzyne intermediates" [186] in nucleophilic aromatic substitution, *cf.* eqn. (52).

Benzyne
intermediate

2. *Cis*-Elimination

In certain suitably constructed compounds overall *cis*-elimination can be demonstrated. This could be the stereochemical result of an E1cB or E2(E1cB-like) mechanism or it could be due to a distinct highly-concerted *cis*-bimolecular mechanism: a choice between these possibilities is often difficult.

One-step processes proceeding through a 4-centred planar transition state (XXXIIa) to give *cis*-elimination are very improbable for E1 reactions, since the stereochemistry of, and the effect of changing conditions on, these reactions cannot be interpreted on this model. In certain cases when X contains a basic group, such a mechanism is possible in non-polar media at elevated temperatures and will be discussed in Chapter 7. Similarly, a bimolecular mechanism involving a transition state, (**XXXIIb**) which contains an ion-pair of the base molecule, must be completely rejected for

(XXXIIa)   (XXXIIb)

alkoxides in protic solvents. Such a process is feasible in non-polar media, particularly for bases such as metal-alkyls and amides, but a *trans*-elimination occurs for the decomposition of certain tosylates with lithium aluminium hydride in ether *[139, 187, 188]*, and studies are lacking in other systems. The well-known dehydrohalogenation method for steroids using lithium chloride in dimethylformamide has been considered to utilise a cyclic transition state *[90]*, but ion-pairing seems unlikely in a good solvating medium of such high dielectric constant and recent kinetic studies have indicated a *trans*-E2 mechanism *[92]*. Experiments on the 1,2-diphenyl-1-propyl systems, similar to those described in Chap. 1, sect. 3, would be valuable for all these conditions.

The electrostatic interaction between negatively-charged bases and positively-charged leaving groups should be much larger in a solvent of low polarity than in the hydroxylic solvents normally used, and such attraction could favour a *cis*-mechanism. This orientation does occur for the reaction in *tert*-butanol mentioned on p. 88, but other data are not available, although suspensions of alkoxides in benzene and solutions of sodium in pentyl and hexyl alcohols have been used in preparative eliminations from 'onium salts, where they are found to give better yields than the normal Hofmann degradation procedures—probably because of the feebler solvating power of the medium towards the anions.

It seems that in special structures the necessity for *trans*-elimination is not completely dominant and *cis*-elimination can appear, if not as the major stereochemical result, at least as an important one. Several such instances have been discovered in cyclic structures, but it is very difficult to decide whether E2 (ElcB-like) or two-step ElcB mechanisms are involved. Probably the earliest example of such a reaction is eqn. (53) *[189]*: the major product is

$$(53)$$

the result of *trans*-elimination, but the other product is from *cis*-elimination. However it is possible that the minor product is formed by the *trans*-decomposition of an initially-formed quinolinium salt. Several kinetic studies *[139, 190]* have revealed that under less extreme conditions, only *trans*-products were formed.

Bordwell and Cristol and their co-workers have studied the kinetics and products of base-promoted eliminations of several *cis*- and *trans*-1,2-disubstituted cyclohexanes and -pentanes with various leaving groups X and with strongly electron-attracting groups Y, such as $\cdot SO_2Ph$, $\cdot SO_2C_6H_4CH_3 \cdot SO_3$, and $\cdot$ Ph situated β to these, and some examples for the reaction (54) are shown in Table 11 in which the results for β-benzene hexachloride, which contains a

$$(54)$$

TABLE 11

ELIMINATION RATES FROM *cis*- AND *trans*-1,2-DISUBSTITUTED
CYCLOHEXANES

Ring	X	Y	Rate of trans-elim.[*] / Rate of cis-elim.	Ref.
1. β-Benzene hexachloride	·Cl	·Cl	7,000–24,000[**]	31, 32
2. Cyclohexyl	·OSO$_2$C$_7$H$_7$	·SO$_2$C$_7$H$_7$	435	194
3. Cyclohexyl	·$\overset{+}{\text{S}}$Me$_2$	·Ph	383	192
4. Cyclohexyl	·$\overset{+}{\text{N}}$Me$_3$	·Ph	133	192
5. Cyclopentyl	·OSO$_2$C$_7$H$_7$	·SO$_2$C$_7$H$_7$	20	194
6. Cyclopentyl	·O$\overset{-}{\text{S}}$O$_3$	·$\overset{-}{\text{S}}$O$_3$	Only *cis* studied	195

[*] The rate of *trans*-elimination from the *cis*-isomer and *vice-versa*.
[**] Dependent on the experimental conditions.

much weaker electron-attracting substituent group, are also included. In several cases (*e.g.* with the Ph-substituents) it has been
shown that the kinetically controlled products are obtained, and
elimination and subsequent isomerisation to a more stable conjugated olefin are excluded *[191–193]*. The β-hydrogen which is
activated by the electron-withdrawing substituent is lost in all
cases; even for the *trans*-1,2-isomers which would be expected to
undergo *trans*-elimination towards C$_6$. This alternative product
(XXXII) has never been isolated, and so although *cis*-elimination
is much slower than *trans*-removal of the same activated hydrogen,
it must be at least 50–100 times faster than the *trans*-removal of a
hydrogen which is not activated. These observations can be
rationalised in terms of E2 mechanisms on conformational arguments, the basis of which will be considered more fully in Chap. 5,
sect. 2. The *trans*-isomer will have both its bulky 1- and 2-sub-
stituents in equatorial conformations in the ground state, but to
achieve a E2 *trans*-planar elimination towards C$_6$, both of these

groups have to be forced into axial positions which greatly increases the activation energy required to reach this state, and prevents its competition with possible *cis*-mechanisms in which such strain will not occur. The *cis*-isomer will possess the bulkier of its 1,2-substituents in an equatorial orientation, and the other in an axial. The tendency for the leaving X-group to be in an axial conformation in the cyclohexanes of Table 11 should be in the order 1 > 2 > 3 > 4, and in the last cases this group should be predominantly equatorial. In order for *trans*-elimination to occur from the *cis*-isomer towards either the activated C_2-position or the unactivated C_6, the 1-group will have to assume an axial conformation, and again this will require an expenditure of energy which will increase in the order of 1 to 4. In particular the increase in energy on forcing a large $-\overset{+}{N}Me_3$ group into an axial position may be about 5 kcal.mole^{-1}*. However, the energy increase will not be as much as would occur in *trans*-isomers for elimination towards C_6, for the other 2-linked group will now assume an equatorial conformation, not an axial one. If the energy to attain *cis*-elimination from the *trans*-isomer is about the same in these compounds, these differences in the ease of *trans*-elimination from the *cis*-isomers will account for the decreasing rate ratios in the last column of Table 11. The cyclopentyl examples react slightly faster than their cyclohexyl analogues owing to a removal of eclipsed bonds on reaction. The low *trans/cis* ratio seems difficult to explain, and further studies with other leaving groups are necessary.

The favoured elimination of the hydrogen attached to C_2, even at the luxury of some kind of *cis*-elimination process, is probably also due to the presence of the powerfully electron-attracting group at this carbon atom which favours an E1cB-like transition state: and under certain conditions a chlorine substituent can also show this effect, *cf.* eqn. (53), and groups such as $\cdot NO_2$, $\cdot CN$, $\cdot COOR$ and $p\text{-}NO_2C_6H_4$ would also undoubtedly do so. Another explanation of these phenomena is the incursion of E1cB mechanisms [196], which would be especially favoured by these substituents and which

---

* This may be an excessive estimate, *cf.* Chap. 6, sect. 4d.

perhaps could lead directly to olefin from the carbanion or could invert the configuration at the β-carbon as in eqn. (55) and so enable normal *trans*-elimination to occur; but the workers foremost in this field prefer [194] a synchronous one-step mechanism for

$$
\begin{array}{c}
\underset{\substack{| \quad |\\ X \quad H}}{\overset{\substack{H \quad Y\\ | \quad |}}{-\text{C}-\text{C}-}} \quad
\underset{\overline{\text{H}_2\text{O}}}{\overset{\overline{\text{OH}}}{\rightleftharpoons}} \quad
\underset{\substack{| \quad |\\ X \quad \ominus}}{\overset{\substack{H \quad Y\\ | \quad |}}{-\text{C}-\text{C}-}} \quad
\overset{\text{fast}}{\rightleftharpoons} \quad
\underset{\substack{| \quad |\\ X \quad Y}}{\overset{\substack{H \quad \ominus\\ | \quad |}}{-\text{C}-\text{C}-}} \quad
\underset{\overline{\text{OH}}}{\overset{\text{H}_2\text{O}}{\rightleftharpoons}} \quad
\underset{\substack{| \quad |\\ X \quad Y}}{\overset{\substack{H \quad H\\ | \quad |}}{-\text{C}-\text{C}-}} \quad (55)
\end{array}
$$

$$\downarrow \qquad\qquad\qquad \downarrow \qquad\qquad\qquad \downarrow$$

Olefin   Olefin   Olefin

cis-elimination as well as for *trans*. This preference was originally based on the lack of deuterium uptake into the unreacted substrate [161, 197] and on the general acid catalysis [194] which were observed in every case which was examined. These criteria, however, do not completely exclude a non-equilibrium two-step process, but only mean that any carbanion must have a half-life of less than 10^{-9} sec (*cf.* p. 82). The rates of deuterium exchange in alkaline solution at the α-position of cyclopentyl and cyclohexyl-p-tolylsulphones have been measured [198] and found to be from 10^3 to 10^5 times slower than the *cis*-elimination rates of the corresponding *trans*-β-substituted tosylates, and this was held to exclude E1cB processes. This deduction is probably correct, for an inversion of configuration is necessary if the normal geometrical requirements for elimination apply to such an exothermic process as the decomposition of a carbanion formed from a *trans*-disubstituted compound, *cf.* eqn. (55), and recently it has been shown [199] that carbanions which are stabilised by a neighbouring sulphone group can retain their configuration, and hydrogen exchange can be up to 2000-fold faster than inversion. Comparison of the rates of base-catalysed elimination, racemisation, and β-deuterium exchange for other types of compound possessing asymmetric β-carbon atoms would be worthwhile. The rate of deuterium exchange has been shown to be consistent with the rate of elimination in an example (dehydrofluorination) especially favourable for E1cB [468], but recent Hammett correlations in related series *[469]* suggest a one-step highly-concerted elimination process.

If two-step mechanisms do not occur the incidence of *cis*-elimination in cyclic compounds must be attributed to the conformational restrictions to *trans*-elimination that have already been discussed. Unconvincing attempts *[200]* have been made to explain the facilitation of concerted *cis*-elimination in terms of electrostatic influences between the leaving groups and the base in structures which are held semi-rigid in ring systems, such as pictured in (XXXIII). Examples of *cis*-elimination in tosylates and 'onium

(XXXIII)   (XXXIV)   (XXXV)

compounds can also be accommodated by special explanations (see Chap. 2, sect. 2c and Chap. 4, sect. 4).

Conformational and electrostatic influences should be negligible in straight-chain compounds, for there should only be small energy barriers to rotation into the conformation for *trans*-elimination. The diastereoisomers of (XXXIV) *[174, 200]*, which might be expected to undergo E1cB or E2 (E1cB-like) mechanisms in view of the electron-withdrawing β-sulphone group, were found to decompose with complete *trans*-stereospecificity. This shows that either a concerted process occurred or that any carbanion intermediate, which largely would be formed from conformations similar to (XXXV)*, must be able to rotate into such an orientation that the lone-pair of electrons on the β-carbon could eject the α-bonded group in the usual *trans*-manner, for inversion of the configuration

---

* Steric hindrance to proton abstraction from any conformation should be negligible (*cf*. Chap. 3, sect. 4b).

at C_β would not give a stereospecific *trans*-result. A carbanion can retain its configuration during certain reactions, especially when a neighbouring sulphone group is present, but a stability that could survive a rotation about a C–C bond seems doubtful, for even relatively stable carbonium ions are believed to be neutralised or to decompose before rotation about a C–C bond, or inversion at the carbon centre, can occur [201], and an E2 concerted process is to be preferred. If an E1cB process were occurring, the half-life of the carbanion could be considerably longer than the rotation time, and if it was longer than 10^{-9} sec the isotope exchange and general base catalysis criteria might be applicable: such experiments have not been performed in this system.

The main difficulty of assigning *cis*-E2 mechanisms to the cyclic substrates is the relatively small energy differences (*cf.* with the benzene hexachlorides) between these and the *trans*-processes. Such a difference can be reasonably accounted for on conformational arguments previously mentioned, but also a synchronous E2 process possessing an E1cB-like transition state could occur. The latter explanation accommodates the anomalous elimination from *meso*-dichlorosuccinic acid which gives the *cis*-elimination product (chlorofumaric acid) on bimolecular decomposition under acidic or basic conditions. In this case the relative advancement of deprotonation was attributed to the potential prototropy caused by the carboxyl groups [197].

cis-Elimination may appear in acyclic structures when the anti-conformation for E2 cannot be achieved owing to steric hindrance. $(t\text{-Bu})_2\text{CHCH}_2\overset{+}{\text{N}}\text{Me}_3\overline{\text{O}}\text{H}$ must largely exist in the conformation (XXXVI), and although rotation into the anti-position is greatly

(XXXVI)

restricted, yet it gives an enhanced yield of olefin compared with those obtained from less ramified β,β'-dialkylated homologues [202]. Such predominance of elimination suggests a specially facilitated cis-process, for the competing substitution at the methyl groups should not be greatly hindered and should have a rate similar to that in the lower homologues (kinetic studies are not reported). Perhaps the large electrostatic interaction between the charged 'onium group and the β-proton, which are held in proximity, induces an ElcB-type mechanism; or an α'-β mechanism (this will be discussed shortly in sect. 4) may take place. Either of these would be facilitated by the relief of steric strain that must occur on olefin formation.

Several cases [203] of overall cis-eliminations in structures possessing neighbouring carbonyl groups are undoubtedly due to the now ready carbanion formation or to enolisation and subsequent inversion of the configuration of the β-hydrogen atom which is then eliminated in a normal trans-process, eqn. (56).

(56)

3. α-Elimination

A possible mechanism for overall β-elimination involves the initial loss of α-hydrogen, followed by migration of a hydrogen or another group from the β-position either before, concurrent with, or after the loss of the other α-fragment. Such a scheme involving only carbanions, eqn. (57A) is unlikely since migration to a negative centre would be required and this process is not observed in these

(A) $RR'CHCH_2X \rightleftharpoons RR'CH\bar{C}HX \longrightarrow RR'C:CH_2 + RCH:CHR'$

$\Big\downarrow{-\bar{X}}$ (57)

(B) $RR'CHCH:$

ions (*cf.* neopentyl, neophyl, etc.)—at least in protic solvents. A carbene-forming process, eqn. (57B) is more probable, for chloroform is known to decompose thus, and carbenes have been established as intermediates in other reactions [204].

The initial loss of an α-hydrogen has been demonstrated as the first step of overall α-elimination processes and in cases where olefin formation or rearrangement cannot occur dipolar molecules— "ylides" (XXXVII)—of varying stability have been found [205].

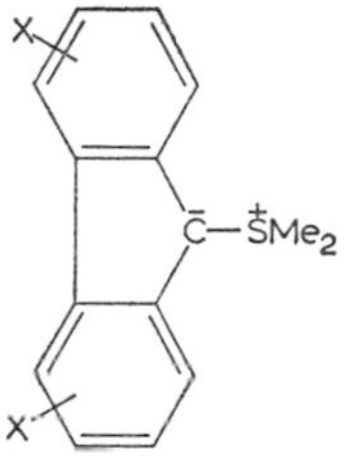

(X=H,NO₂)

(XXXVII)

Moreover, α-hydrogen abstraction is known to be rapid for structures possessing α-bonded ·C:O, ·NO₂, ·CN, ·SO₂Ph, and ·Ph, since such hydrogen will readily exchange with a deuterated solvent in weakly alkaline or sometimes even in neutral conditions. And unsubstituted sulphonium compounds will exchange faster than they will eliminate; although the corresponding ammonium compounds exchange at a rate 10^6-fold less and much slower than they decompose [43a, 206]. This difference between the two similar classes is due to d-orbital resonance in the former structure, eqn. (58)

which stabilises the formation of the anion, but which cannot occur in the latter as nitrogen does not possess $3d$-orbitals of low energy and so cannot expand its octet to 10 electrons. Despite this ease of carbanion formation in certain classes of compound, the ejection of an α-linked group with its bond electrons to leave a carbene would probably be a relatively slow process (as it is in the decomposition of chloroform) and most indications are that α-elimination cannot compete with the more usual mechanisms in protic solvents and in most aprotic ones. Thus, optically active $CH_3CHPh\overset{+}{N}Me_3\bar{I}$ has been recovered unracemised from a reaction which had progressed halfway to completion [55], and this within the limits discussed for the similar type of diagnostic test for E1cB, eliminates a mechanism of type (57), the first step of which is reversible. Also products of rearrangement with elimination and of cyclisation have not been detected for Me_3CCH_2X and Ph_3CCH_2X under E2 conditions in hydroxylic solvents. However, no studies have been carried out on sulphonium salts which should be potentially favourable, although the close similarity of elimination from both types of 'onium compounds would indicate that each class utilised a similar mechanism. Tracer and optical studies on α-phenylethylsulphonium compounds would be interesting as this structure should be particularly suitable for α-eliminations because the α-phenyl group would especially stabilise the transition state leading to carbanion formation.

Most of the other evidence for the unimportance of these processes also does not refer to sulphonium compounds. Thus although α-exchange was detected [43a] in the decomposition of $CD_3CH_2\overset{+}{N}Me_3\bar{O}H$ in glycol at 180°, it was always found that, when allowance was made for exchange with the solvent, the olefin which was formed contained one less deuterium atom than the substrate, and so α-migration could not have occurred: similar results were obtained from tritium tracer studies [207].

When β-substituents which can separate as anions are present in sulphonium salts, the direction of elimination may be changed and the α-hydrogen and the β-group can be lost, eqn. (59), in what might be a synchronous E2 process or one involving prior α-elimination.

$$X\overset{\frown}{}CH_2-\underset{\underset{H}{\overset{\backslash}{|}}}{CH}-\overset{+}{S}Me_2 \xrightarrow[25°]{\overline{O}H} \bar{X} + CH_2=CH\overset{+}{S}Me_2 + \overset{+}{H} \xrightarrow[100°]{\overline{O}H} CH\equiv CH \quad (59)$$

Such a reaction occurs for X = PhCOO and PhO, which are readily capable of forming negative ions; β-linked MeS· and PhCONH· gave the normal E2 type process in which a β-hydrogen was lost, and with PhCH$_2$NH only substitution took place [121, 208]. The role of the sulphur atom in labilising the α-hydrogen is shown by the non-occurrence of these reactions when the corresponding ammonium salts were used, although the inductive effect of this group should now be greater.

It has been suggested [209] that α-elimination may occur with strong bases such as KNH$_2$ and PhLi in non-hydroxylic solvents but that for alkoxide bases in hydroxylic solvents activated structures and elevated temperatures are required. The second conclusion is probably correct, but until recently there seemed little evidence for the first. Thus the reactions of Et$_2$CDCH$_2$Br, Me$_2$CDCH$_2$Br, and CH$_3$(CH$_2$)$_5$CD$_2$CH$_2$Br with KNH$_2$ in liquid ammonia gave olefins which contained no deuterium in the first two cases and only 1 atom per molecule in the last, and this excluded α-processes [210]. Also, phenyl-sodium in ether can decompose certain ethers (particularly aromatics) as in eqn. (60), but in some examples only α-metallation

$$\overset{+}{Na}\overset{-}{Ph} + H—\overset{|}{\underset{|}{C}}—\overset{|}{\underset{|}{C}}—O—R \longrightarrow PhH + \overset{|}{\underset{|}{C}}=\overset{|}{\underset{|}{C}} + \overset{+}{Na}\overset{-}{O}R \qquad (60)$$

occurred, and so a carbanion was not necessarily a precursor of the elimination process. This reaction was thus concluded to be a synchronous E2, and studies [211] of suitably substituted alkyl cyclohexyl ethers showed that cis-elimination occurred by reaction with an ion-pair (cf. p. 144). An example of α-elimination could be the decomposition of PhCHCH$_3$CH$_2$Br with sodium amide in xylene at 180° to form both PhCCH$_3$:CH$_2$ and CH$_3$CH:CHPh [212]; but the latter olefin may have arisen from the isomerisation of the other under these forcing conditions, for when the reaction was carried out in liquid ammonia at —33° only the normal β-elimination product was obtained [213].

Despite this apparent lack of evidence for α-elimination, recent studies have shown [214–217] that carbene-forming processes

can occur in aprotic media under certain conditions. Olefins and cyclic hydrocarbons are formed in Wurtz-type reactions of alkali metals and metal-alkyls with alkyl halides in inert solvents and much dispute has arisen over the relative importance of ionic and radical mechanisms. Recently, tracer studies of certain reactions (61) have been carried out [218] under conditions believed to be

$$\underset{CH_3}{\overset{CH_3}{>}}CHCH_2X \xrightarrow{\text{B:}} CH_3-CH-CH_2 \ (35\%) + \underset{CH_3}{\overset{CH_3}{>}}C=CH_2 \ (65\%) \quad (61)$$

$$\text{(A)} \quad \overset{|}{CH_2} \qquad\qquad \text{(B)}$$

heterolytic: B can be formed by α- or β-elimination and A either by carbene formation and intramolecular insertion or by removal of a γ-hydrogen and nucleophilic attack by the resulting ionic centre on the α-carbon. Both sets of alternatives can be distinguished by labelling α-, β-, or γ-hydrogens and determining the content and distribution of tracer in the products. It was found that some α-elimination occurred with PhLi as base, and much less with $NaNH_2$, but when similar reactions were studied with methoxide in methanol up to 10% of the total reaction proceeded through the (presumed) carbene-type mechanisms [219]. If these experiments have been interpreted correctly, and if such results are general, there will have to be a re-interpretation of the views on this mechanism in protic solvents.

Certain other types of eliminations may involve carbenes. The base-promoted decomposition of p-toluenesulphonyl-hydrazones of ketones may be one such case [220], eqn. (62A), but the stereochemistry of rearrangement in decalins, the lack of insertion products, and the observation that for sec-butyl compounds the product ratio of olefins is different from that for known carbene

$$\text{(A)} \quad R=N-NHSO_2C_7H_7 \xrightarrow{\bar{B}} \bar{R}-N=N-SO_2C_7H_7 \rightarrow R: \rightarrow \text{Products}$$

$$\downarrow \qquad\qquad\qquad \nearrow \text{(olefins, etc.)}$$

$$\text{(B)} \quad \left\{ \begin{array}{l} RH-N=N-SO_2C_7H_7 \\ R=\overset{+}{N}=\bar{N}, \ RH-\overset{+}{N}_2 \end{array} \right\} \qquad (62)$$

processes indicate that E1 or E2 processes, eqn. (62B) similar to diazotisation-deaminations may occur [221, 222].

Studies in dipolar aprotic solvents, in which basic properties are much enhanced, may enable α, E1cB and α'-β (see sect. 4) mechanisms to be isolated. A specially favourable medium may be tetramethylenesulphone, for it has been shown by indicator measurements that a solution of $PhNMe_3OH$ in a 95% mixture of this with 5% of water gives a solution 10^7 times more basic than the corresponding solution in water [223]. Mechanisms which are of negligible importance in water might appear in this medium and new methods of preparation, and of acid and base catalysis, might be made available.

4. α'-β-Elimination

Probably a more important process, the scope of which has not yet been fully explored, is the α'-β mechanism discovered by Wittig [224]. In this, an α-hydrogen of an 'onium compound is removed by a base to form a dipolar ylide; the negative end of which then abstracts a β-hydrogen from another branch of the substrate by means of a cyclic transition state. The decomposition of the ylide can be either one-, or (less likely) two-step, as shown in

$$(63)$$

eqn. (63). In the former, cis-elimination must occur, but the latter will have an overall orientation dependent on the stability of the second carbanion.

Such processes are found in aprotic media with metal-alkyls as bases, and a typical example is the sequence (64) which occurs in ether with phenyl-lithium to give an isolable intermediate [225].

$$\tag{64}$$

β-Eliminations, in which an ylide molecule acts as a base to attack an 'onium ion are also possible in these conditions. Ylides have been isolated for straight chain and cycloalkyls, and heterocyclics, but elimination only occurred when 5-membered cyclic transition states could be achieved; in other cases the reaction stopped after the first step. Only metal-alkyls were efficient promoters; with metal-amides and alkoxides, β-elimination mainly prevailed [224c].

Rings larger than cycloheptyl can show *cis-trans* mono-olefin isomerism (see Chap. 5, sect. 4) and the α'-β decomposition of cyclo-octyl 'onium salts gave mainly the *cis*-isomer (*cf.* Table 12),

TABLE 12

cis-trans-OLEFINS FROM CYCLO-OCTYL STRUCTURES

Compound and reagent	Yield (%)		Ref.
	cis	trans	
(a) Ammonium iodide, PhLi (ether)	80	+ 20	224b
(b) Ammonium iodide, KNH₂ (liq. NH₃)	15	+ 85	224b
(c) Ammonium iodide, Hofmann degrad.	40	+ 60	226
(d) Xanthate, acetate esters, thermal decomp.	100	+ 0	470
(e) Sulphonium iodide, various bases (in aprotic media)	100	+ 0	228

rather than the *trans*-isomer which is predominantly formed in β-eliminations involving Hofmann degradation or potassamide as base. However, the known stereospecific *cis*-eliminations of the esters gave entirely *cis*-olefin[*] and this would be formed via a 5-membered cyclic *syn*-clinal conformation very similar to that adopted in any α'-β-process: it seems that the 20% yield of *trans*-olefin from the ammonium salt and phenyl-lithium must have arisen from intruding β-processes, rather than from any relaxation of the stereochemical requirements of an α'-β-transition state.

The extension of this mechanism to elimination from 'onium salts in other solvents is obvious, and although in protic conditions the ylide would be rapidly neutralised by the solvent, it is possible that reaction could proceed through a small equilibrium concentration of this species, especially in the sulphonium series where the carbanion would be stabilised by d-orbital resonance.

A criterion for this mechanism is to carry out the reaction with a substrate labelled at the β-position with a hydrogen isotope and to examine the α-leaving group (NMe_3 or SMe_2) for the presence of tracer (due allowance being made for the possibility of exchange of the leaving group with the solvent after elimination). Such a study was made for the pyrolysis of $CH_3CH_2\overset{+}{N}Me_3\overline{O}H$ using deuterium as tracer [227] and it was shown that no α'-β-mechanism was detectable up to 150°: previous workers [207] had claimed such a process for this substrate, but had used a faulty experimental technique. When, however, treated with a metal alkyl in an aprotic medium, this compound and also $(CH_2)_5CHCH_2\overset{+}{N}Me_3\overline{X}$ exhibited far-reaching proton shifts which were attributable to either α- or α'-β-processes. The α'-β' mechanism has been established for one sulphonium compound in aprotic solvents [228], (*cf.* eqn. (65)), *e.g.* NMR studies have proved that only the isomers shown were

$$(CH_3CD_2)_3\overset{+-}{SI} \xrightarrow[\text{ether}]{Ph_3\overline{C}Na^+} \begin{array}{c} CH_2\!-\!CD_2 \\ | \quad\quad \diagdown\overset{+}{S}CD_2CH_3 \\ H \quad CD\diagup \\ | \\ CH_3 \end{array} \longrightarrow \begin{array}{c} CH_2\!:\!CD_2 \\ + \\ CH_3CD_2SCHDCH_3 \end{array} \quad (65)$$

---

[*] Note that stereospecific *cis*-elimination can form either *cis*- or *trans*-cyclo-olefins in these systems.

formed and α- or β-elimination would require a different distribution of tracer. The only similar study involving hydroxylic media is the decomposition of β-phenylethylsulphonium salts. This should be an especially favourable case for this mechanism: but preliminary results indicate its non-occurrence [229].

The α'-β mechanism thus undoubtedly plays a very minor role in hydroxylic solvents, although it may occur in structures which cannot easily attain the *trans*-conformation. There is no evidence for the required *cis*-elimination in 'onium compounds; and a cyclic transition state would be expected by analogy with the amine-oxide and other cases to stimulate either Saytzeff-type or undecisive orientation, rather than the observed Hofmann rule, whereas in fact, it is for the 'onium compounds that the latter rule is most rigidly observed. Also such cyclic states should require a large negative entropy of formation—in contrast to the very high positive values found in 'onium decompositions. In aprotic media the mechanism seems likely, for here carbanions are not easily neutralised. Pyrolyses of the syrupy hydrates during Hofmann degradations could well simulate these conditions and tracer studies of these decompositions would be rewarding.

The *cis*-eliminations in 2-phenyl-'onium-cyclohexanes, which were discussed in the last section, could also be interpreted by an α'-β mechanism. The alternative of α-elimination leading to the inversion of configuration at the α-carbon has been eliminated by tracer studies [471]. Recently it has been shown, by tracer experiments, that the *cis*-elimination from the *trans*-'onium salt in 95% ethanol with alkali did not involve an α'-β process [230]; but studies have not been carried out under pyrolytic Hofmann conditions, and these would be more significant.

5. δ- and γ-Eliminations

The former can occur in special structures and may involve the rearrangement of a double bond (*cf.* eq. (8), Chap. 1). One of the few quantitative studies of such reactions has shown [231] that the base-catalysed and thermal aromatisations of the *trans*-disubstituted anthracenes (XXXVIII) (X = OH, OBz, OAc) react up to 1200-fold faster than the *cis*-isomers (**XXXIX, XL**). The

(XXXVIII)   (XXXIX)   (XL)

aromatic rings probably hold the central skeleton in a deformed boat-like structure (*cf.* Chap. 5, sect. 6), which in the *trans*-compound allows two trans-planar type "eliminations" to proceed with favourable orbital overlap; a situation which cannot be achieved in either conformation of the other isomer.

Other 1,4-processes occur in 3-hydroxytosylcyclohexanes *[232]*,

$$(66)$$

eqn. (66) and in the vinylogous degradations of curare alkaloids *[233]*, eqn. (67): here octets are preserved by ring fissions.

$$(67)$$

γ-Processes can sometimes occur for activated γ-hydrogens in the presence of a strong base (*cf.* eqn. (68)): either carbanion or carbene formation followed by cyclisation may be involved *[234, 235]*.

$$\text{PhCH}_2\text{CH}_2\text{CH}_2\overset{+}{\text{N}}\text{Me}_3\bar{\text{I}} \xrightarrow{\text{KNH}_2, \text{NH}_3} \text{Ph}-\text{CH}\underset{\diagdown\text{CH}_2\diagup}{-\!\!-\!\!-}\text{CH}_2 \quad (80\%) \quad (68)$$

6. Trans-annular Elimination

Prelog, Cope, and others have studied a "non-classical" process which can occur in ring systems of 8–12 members under certain conditions [236]. In such rings, a conformation can be easily achieved [237] such that two carbon atoms which are separated by a chain of several other atoms are forced into close proximity, and the formation of a carbonium-ion centre at one atom can lead to bonding between them and also to hydride-ion shift with resulting trans-annular substitution or elimination. The situation can be schematically represented as in eqn. (69); and is found in certain

$$(69)$$

A: Trans-annular elimination
B: Trans-annular elimination and substitution following hydride-ion shift
C: Normal substitution and elimination

deaminations, Hofmann degradations, and solvolyses of tosylates.
  Such mechanisms have been elucidated by means of product, ^{14}C, and deuterium tracer studies; and hydride shifts from C_3, C_4, C_5, or C_6 can occur in different systems, although alkyl shifts have not been detected. The ionisation and hydride shift are not concerted, and a transient carbonium ion exists; but the driving forces are rather obscure. Some possibilities for the latter will be considered in Chap. 6, sect. 6.

7. Fragmentation

Eliminations involving β-groups other than single atoms have been studied in the last few years, mainly by Grob, and have been the subject of two excellent reviews *[238, 239]*. When a group of atoms can split off from this position, a substantial proportion of the substrate may be lost and the process is called a fragmentation. The β-fragment, which is often a positive ion, is usually unstable and will subsequently decompose by substitution or elimination. In general, the reaction can be represented as in eqn. (70); where

$$a—b—c—d—X \longrightarrow a—\overset{+}{b} + c=d + \bar{X} \qquad (70)$$

a can be alkyl, aryl, OH, OR, NR_2 or typically a group which can donate electrons by an inductive or electromeric mechanism; b is usually carbon and X is a halogen, 'onium or ester group.

About 30 examples are known, and three important types, eqns. (71)–(73), are represented below. The first two do not require the presence of a base, and are unimolecular decompositions of the

$$(CH_3)_3CCH_2CH_2X \longrightarrow (CH_3)_3\overset{+}{C} + CH_2:CH_2 + X \longrightarrow$$
$$(CH_3)_2C:CH_2 + (CH_3)_3COH \qquad (71)$$

$$R_2NCR_2CH_2CH_2X \longrightarrow R_2\overset{+}{N}=CR_2 + CH_2:CH_2 + \bar{X} \longrightarrow R_2NH + R_2C:O \qquad (72)$$

$$HOCH_2CMe_2CH_2Br \xrightarrow[\bar{O}H]{} \bar{O}CH_2CMe_2CH_2Br \longrightarrow$$
$$CH_2O + Me_2C:CH_2 + B\bar{r} \qquad (73)$$

limiting types of the processes which cause the *tert.*-butyl hyperconjugation and rearrangement discussed in Chapter 3. The last example involves base catalysis, but only to form an electron-releasing group attached to the γ-carbon atom, and it is similar in mechanism to the decarboxylations of β-keto and β-halo acids.

The kinetics of decomposition of γ-amino halides and esters have been studied, and the fragmentation has been shown to proceed either by a synchronous or by a two-step process. If the lone-pair on the nitrogen is suitably orientated to allow a synchronous mechanism, the substrate will solvolyse at a rate greatly in excess of that of similar alkyl structures to give almost entirely fragmentation products in a manner which resembles the well-known neighbouring-group effects in rearrangement and solvolysis. If such a stereochemistry cannot be achieved, non-accelerated ionisation at the α-carbon occurs and a mixture of fragmentation, elimination, and substitution is obtained.

An example of the acceleration afforded by a synchronous mechanism is shown by the solvolysis (74). In such a cyclic system a "fragmentation" process does not actually produce fragments, but the bond changes are analogous to those considered before. This reaction is almost as fast as that of *tert*-butyl bromide under the same conditions, and is 50,000 times faster than reaction (75), in which fragmentation cannot occur, and which shows the typical low reactivity of a bridgehead compound towards solvolysis.

$$\begin{array}{c} \text{N---CH}_2\text{---CH}_2\text{---C---Br} \end{array} \xrightarrow{\text{EtOH}} \begin{array}{c} \text{CH}_2\text{=}\overset{+}{\text{N}} \end{array} \text{C=CH}_2 + \bar{\text{B}}\text{r} \quad (74)$$

$$\begin{array}{c} \text{CH---CH}_2\text{---CH}_2\text{---C---Br} \end{array} \xrightarrow{\text{EtOH}} \begin{array}{c} \text{CH---CH}_2\text{---CH}_2\text{---C---OR} + \bar{\text{B}}\text{r} \quad (75)$$

In only a few cases has a one-step fragmentation involving attack by a base on a β-bonded group been achieved [240, 241]. One probable example is eqn. (76).

$$\bar{\text{O}}\text{H} + \text{SiH}_3\text{CH}_2\text{CH}_2\text{Cl} \longrightarrow \text{SiH}_3\text{OH} + \text{CH}_2\text{:CH}_2 + \bar{\text{X}} \quad (76)$$

Chapter 5

ELIMINATION IN CYCLIC SYSTEMS

Up to now the general features of eliminations have been discussed. This chapter and the next will be devoted to a survey of these reactions in special structures and in particular types of compounds of theoretical and practical importance.

Cyclic systems have been already considered in several examples, but the special stereochemistry which here arises and the illuminating adaptations to the general scheme which can occur make a separate discussion worthwhile. The outstanding characteristic of these systems is that the geometry can be rigid and so the leaving groups can be introduced by stereospecific procedures into known, fixed, relative positions. The mechanism of reaction is then often framed to fit the structure, rather than as with straight-chain compounds, where the conformation of the molecule can readily be changed by rotation about single bonds in order to fit the mechanism. In this chapter the reactions of cyclic halides, esters, and 'onium salts will be considered: dehydrations and deaminations will be discussed subsequently.

1. Hofmann Degradation and General Topics

In the middle of the last century, Hofmann developed the general method of β-elimination, which he had summarised in his rule, into a technique for the degradation of naturally occurring nitrogen bases to olefins with the liberation of nitrogen-containing fragments. He, and others, realised that the olefin could then be oxidised or otherwise converted into recognisable compounds, and so the original structure elucidated. Most of the elimination studies that have been carried out in alicyclic systems have been part of such structural investigations involving the exhaustive methylation of amines to quaternary ammonium hydroxides, and then the Hofmann degradation of these: this technique has also been used for a few naturally occurring straight-chain compounds.

A classical example is the 2-step degradation of pyrollidene, eqn. (77), and such a procedure can be applied to most nitrogen

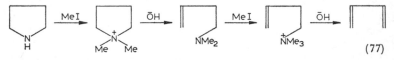

$$(77)$$

bases. An open chain structure requires 1 degradation; one containing a nitrogen linked to 2 carbon atoms needs 2; and a nitrogen at a 3-centred bridgehead requires 3 cycles. This powerful tool has been chiefly applied to the alkaloids, and a recent compilation lists over 220 applications and also includes an excellent discussion of the mechanism, and the experimental techniques used for such reactions [242].

Unfortunately, many of the earlier investigators did not isolate olefins, but hydrogenated the degradation mixture to a paraffin: however, most of their results can be interpreted on the basis of the concepts developed for the model acyclic structures which have previously been discussed. In nearly all cases the degradations must involve E2 decompositions of the 'onium hydroxides, and the actual reaction conditions provide a clue to the structure involved: temperatures well above 100° are usually required for the decomposition of an aqueous or alcoholic solution of an 'onium compound, but β-phenyl substituents will enable reaction to proceed at 100°, and activating β-substituents such as carbonyl groups permit the reaction to proceed at room temperature—perhaps by a "less usual" mechanism.

Rearrangement during degradation is uncommon and does not occur in such likely structures as $Me_3CCHNMe_3CHR'R''$ (R = hydrogen or alkyl) [34, 94], but it sometimes appears in the gymnastic derivatives of the strychnine and morphine series [243]*,

---

* An example of rearrangement in a relatively simple structure has been reported [244], but this is due to the rearrangement of an initially formed β-elimination product.

or when a conjugated olefin can be formed by migration of a double bond. The diene (XLI) from the degradation of piperidine is not isolated, but rearranges immediately to (XLII); and in certain structures the reaction path to the conjugated product may be so facilitated that the Hofmann rule is broken, as in the isoquinolines

(XLI)   (XLII)   (XLIII)

(XLIII) for which the hydrogen at β is initially eliminated. Bredt's rule, (*cf.* sect. 6) and the inductive effect of non-alkyl substituents, must also be considered in discussions of the direction of elimination in cyclic structures. When rearrangement occurs in other cases, an E1 process almost certainly intrudes: such an example is the decomposition of isobornyl 'onium salts in aqueous alkali, eqn. (78) to give mainly camphene (XLIV) with traces of bornylene (XLV) and tricyclene (XLVI) *[100]*, although the small quantities of the last two products could result from β- and trans-annular eliminations respectively.

(XLIV)   (XLV)   (XLVI)   (78)

Some qualitative reports for the decompositions of alicyclics seem peculiar and require re-checking. Thus olefins are not formed in certain apparently favourable cases; and although unimolecular decompositions probably occur (despite the presence of base) in many degradations where olefin yields are low (*cf.* the table in ref. *[242]*), this cannot be the entire explanation. For instance, the tetrahydro-isoquinoline (XLVII) decomposes as anticipated, but the isomeric quinoline (XLVIII) does not form an olefin [245, 246]. The former compound can produce a conjugated olefin, but the latter result is unexpected for although a conjugated system cannot be formed, no elimination occurs even when an α-methyl group is provided [246], although such reaction will occur if the benzene ring is hydrogenated to form the decahydro-salt [247]. Presumably, conjugation between the nitrogen atom and the benzene ring occurs to a greater extent in the transition state for S_N2 decomposition of (XLVIII) than in the alternative E2 transition state (which is probably E1cB-like), and thus the loss of a methyl group is favoured.

(XLVII)   (XLVIII)

Also, it is persistently reported [248] that the decompositions of strychnine alkaloids give better olefin-yields when the 'onium carbonate is used rather than the hydroxide. This seems inexplicable unless the bimolecular decomposition in the latter case consists largely of some reaction other than elimination (as perhaps might occur with so reactive a structure), which does not appear under the former, presumably unimolecular, conditions. It seems very unlikely that the basicity of the carbonate ion is enhanced under these pyrolytic conditions (see Chap. 2, sect. 2b), since it is well known that the 'onium carbonate which is formed if carbon dioxide is not excluded from other hydroxide decompositions yields only a small quantity of olefin on pyrolysis.

Eliminations are also well known in the terpene series from halides, esters, and alcohols, and the detailed geometry of some of these processes will be shortly considered. In complicated structures, factors other than the presence of conjugating substituents could affect the stabilities of the possible olefins, and one could not confidently predict that the "Saytzeff"-product would be formed in these E1 and E2 decompositions. However, such a product invariably* is formed in both the former acidic and latter basic conditions, and this is always the isomer which predominates when the corresponding alcohols are dehydrated under acidic conditions such that an equilibration of the possible products occurs (at least for the examples for which this datum is available). A typical example of orientation in these compounds is eqn. (79): none of the *anti*-Saytzeff product is obtained.

Major   Minor   (79)

2. Conformational Restrictions to Elimination

A brief discussion of conformational analysis is necessary in order to appreciate the factors governing reactions in cyclic systems. Several excellent reviews are available on this topic [249–251].

A cyclohexane molecule exists entirely in the chair form (XLIX) and possesses 6 pairs of differently orientated hydrogens: those lying parallel to the axis of symmetry shown (axial atoms) and those lying almost at right-angles to it (equatorial atoms).

(XLIX)   (L)   (LI)

A substituent can occupy either an axial or an equatorial position, but the separate isomers cannot be isolated for their interconversion requires only about 10 kcal.mole^{-1}, and an activation energy of some 20 kcal.mole^{-1} would be necessary to enable a separation to

---

* Excepting the examples of bornyl-type rearrangements and certain analogous processes.

be carried out by the usual methods. An equilibrium is thus set up between the two forms (L) and (LI) and the introduced group (which is bulky compared to hydrogen) will mainly occupy the equatorial position, for this gives the conformation of lower energy (typically by about 2 kcal.mole^{-1}) in which non-bonding interactions with the ring hydrogen atoms are much less than when the axial position is occupied. If only the axial isomer can react by a particular path, this equilibrium can be easily displaced and so all the substrate will proceed by this path. However, when large substituents such as *tert.*-butyl or trimethylammonium groups are present, the interconversion of the isomers is not so ready, for an energy difference of 5–6 kcal.mole^{-1} has been estimated between the axial and equatorial conformers [252], although recent studies suggest a considerably smaller value [253, 254]. The equilibrium concentration of the former isomer (of higher energy) will now be small and any reaction proceeding through this conformation may be completely obscured by intrinsically slower processes (if these can occur) involving the equatorial form which is present in large excess.

1,2-Disubstituted cyclohexanes can exist as *cis*- or *trans*-isomers, and the conformational equilibria are shown in eqns. (80) and (81). The *cis*-1,2-isomer can exist in two axial-equatorial conformations, and the *trans* in equatorial-equatorial or axial-axial forms. Only

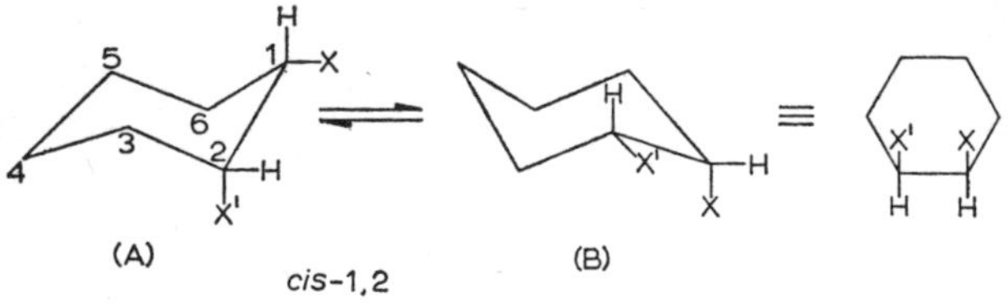

(80)

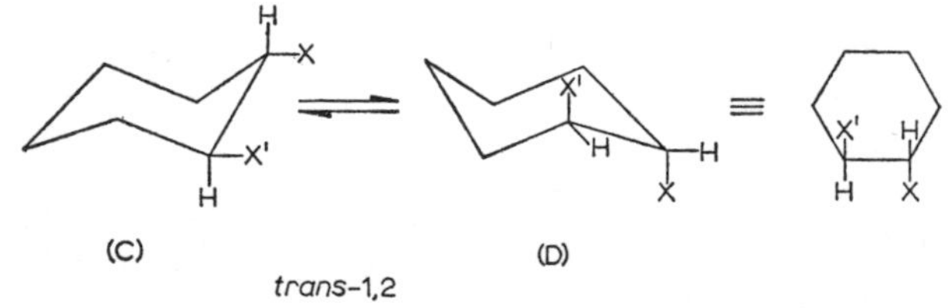

(A)   *cis*-1,2   (B)

(81)

(C)   (D)

trans-1,2

the *cis*-form B can achieve a trans-planar transition state for the elimination of X from C_1 and a hydrogen from C_2, but a similar elimination towards C_6 is stereochemically possible for both B and D. The net result, when allowance is made for the flexibility of the structures, is thus the same as that concluded from the flat models, and so the latter are often used (as in Chapter 4) as representations of the actual situations. What such flat models cannot indicate is the more detailed nature of the relative orientations of X and X'.

Two isomers of decalin exist which result from the fusion of two chair cyclohexane rings in such a way that the hydrogens at the ring junction are *trans* or *cis* (LII), (LIII). The *trans*-linkage imparts a rigidity on the structure because an interconversion of all

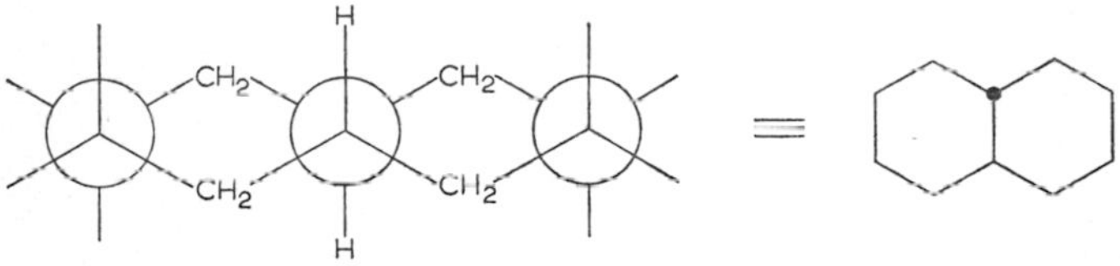

(LII)
trans-isomer

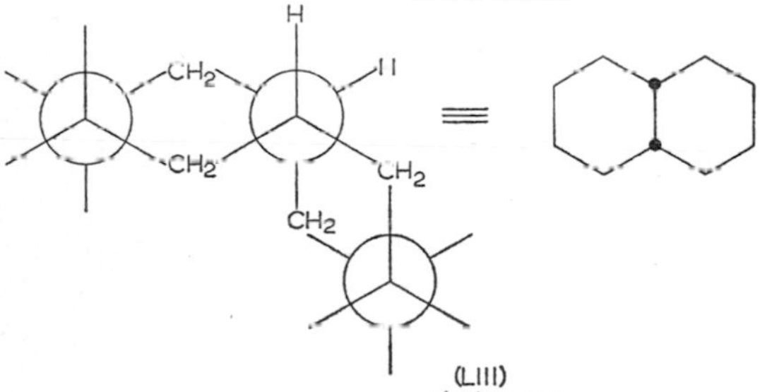

(LIII)
cis-isomer

axial and equatorial bonds cannot be achieved, for to do so would involve forcing the rings into the impossible position of being linked by two adjacent bonds (axial with respect to one ring), which are 180° apart. Substituents in this isomer are thus held rigidly in either axial or equatorial positions, dependent on the methods of synthesis, and such a situation is found particularly in the naturally-occurring steroids and tri-terpenoids, and enables such structures to form excellent models for the testing of the stereo-requirements for various mechanisms. Complete inter-conversion of all bonds can occur in the *cis*-isomer, and unless a very bulky configuration-holding substituent is present equilibria are set up as in cyclohexanes in which both axial and equatorial forms of a substituted compound are present in appreciable amounts.

Other ring systems will not often be considered in the following sections, but the only other case for which detailed conformational data are available is the cyclopentyl skeleton. Here a puckered ring probably exists in either the so-called "half-chair" or "en-velope" forms and conformational orientations are interconvertible. For rings larger than cycloheptyl, the predominance of chair-type structures over boat-forms has not been established, and often it is difficult to predict which form will be the more stable [237]. The interconversion of conformation is probably unrestricted in fused ring-systems of this size owing to the greater flexibility, and any restrictions to β-eliminations involving an inability to attain a trans-planar conformation do not seem to occur.

3. Cyclohexyl and Decalyl Systems

Eliminations are readily observed in these secondary compounds. Unimolecular decomposition gives a moderate olefin proportion (usually with a marked lack of rearrangement products) and bi-molecular elimination is allowed to predominate by a competing substitution which is remarkably slow as compared with sub-stitution in the straight-chain analogues. This last occurrence has been attributed to strain effects due to the 5-coordinated carbon in the transition state, but seems more likely to be caused by steric hindrance of the approach of the base to the ring carbon by the cluster of axial atoms, for it is only from an axial conformation that the substituent can be easily ejected in the usual linear Walden-inversion process. Although an axial substituent is more prone to displacement than is an equatorial one, it is also in an especially

favourable situation for *trans*-elimination and this often predominates. The ease and direction of elimination were originally
used to predict the configurations of the possible isomers of cyclo-
systems, but nowadays preparative techniques and conformational
analysis has enabled the structures of the simplest series, at least,
to be established with a good degree of certainty, and so these
reactions can be discussed as consequences of the stereochemical
requirements of eliminations: they exhibit a magnificent series of
illustrations of the stereospecific *trans*-nature of E2, and the non-
stereospecificity of E1 reactions.

(a) Menthyl compounds

The best studied examples in this sub-class are the isomeric
menthyl and neomenthyl derivatives which possess the structures
(LIV) and (LV) respectively when X is smaller than the isopropyl
group; and the conformation is favoured in which the latter substituent and the 1-methyl group are equatorial.

(LIV)   (LV)   (LVI)

Such a situation exists when X is halogen, but when it is an 'onium
group the alternative conformation for (LV) may predominate in
which the isopropyl group is axial. Conformation (LIV) cannot
achieve a trans-planar transition-state in which X and a hydrogen
bonded either to C_2 or C_4 are involved (the numbering of the
carbons C_1 to C_6 is shown in (LVI)), but after inversion such elimination can occur towards the former position. This explains why
the reaction of menthyl chloride with bases gives only menth-2-ene
(in which the double bond is between C_2 and C_3) and is sluggish
compared with that of the other isomer, for the stable conformation
must be inverted before elimination can occur into a branch which

is not favoured by the electromeric hyperconjugation of the iso-propyl group.

A neomenthyl compound in the conformation shown is suitably arranged for *trans*-elimination in either branch towards C_2 or C_4 and it is found that this chloride will readily react with base to give a mixture of 2- and 3-olefins for which the Saytzeff rule is obeyed. When larger leaving groups are involved, as in 'onium compounds, the stable conformation for the menthyl series will still be (LIV), but for the isomeric series it may be the inverse of (LV) and in this case the attainment of a conformation suitable for elimination will require inversion to a relatively strained structure*. The reaction of the neo-isomer was now found to be sluggish, but still to occur in both branches.

Hückel carried out extensive non-kinetically controlled studies in these series [27], some of which together with more recent results are reported in Table 13. The mechanism shown in brackets is that reasonable for the reaction conditions, and in the other cases it has been verified by kinetic controls which were a necessary precaution because the balance between uni- and bimolecular re-ations is known to be delicately poised for secondary structures such as these, but the non-kinetic assignments are now known to have been correct. Rate data are not shown in the table, but where available they are in accord with the conclusions previously stated. The results elegantly illustrate the stereochemical conclusions just reached. Entries 4–6 show that for leaving groups of different charge-types, no elimination at all occurs in the "forbidden" branch in which a trans-planar transition state cannot be achieved [255, 256], and the experiments with the 'onium compound, which were carried out under kinetically controlled conditions in solution show that the charged leaving group does not favour *cis*-elimination either by means of electrostatic interactions or through α'-β or α-mechanisms. However, Hofmann degradation led to 14% of the 3-isomer. No such restriction occurs for the corresponding neomenthyl compounds (10 and 11) which form both isomeric

---

* The contribution of the 1-methyl group to the steric energies could be elucidated by kinetic studies on isomenthyl and isoneomenthyl compounds.

TABLE 13

ELIMINATION FROM ISOMERIC MENTHYL COMPOUNDS

Example	X	Type	3-ene (%)	2-ene (%)	Orientation[*]	Ref.
1. Menthyl	Cl	E 1	68	32	S	[256]
2. Menthyl	Tosyl	(E 1)	70	30	S	[27]
3. Menthyl	$\overset{+}{N}Me_3$	E 1	68	32	S	[255]
4. Menthyl	Cl	E 2	0	100	super-H	[256]
5. Menthyl	Tosyl	(E 2)	0	100	super-H	[27]
6. Menthyl	$\overset{+}{N}Me_3$	E 2	0	100	super-H	[255]
7. Neomenthyl	Cl	E 1	99	1	super-S	[256]
8. Neomenthyl	Tosyl	(E 1)	100	0	super-S	[27]
9. Neomenthyl	$\overset{+}{N}Me_3$	E 1	98	2	super-S	[255]
10. Neomenthyl	Cl	E 2	75–78	25–22[**]	S	[256]
11. Neomenthyl	$\overset{+}{N}Me_3$	E 2	65–88	35–12[**]	S	[255]

See also
257, 258

[*] S = Saytzeff, H = Hofmann.
[**] Dependent on solvent, base, etc.

menthenes, but what is unexpected is that both of these examples give about the same isomer proportions and that the 'onium compound obeys the Saytzeff rather than the Hofmann rule. This compound, unlike its menthyl isomer, also shows a great tendency to undergo E1 reactions in water, even at large hydroxide concentrations under conditions certainly not expected to favour ionisation of a charged substrate. This tendency gives a clue to the abnormal Saytzeff orientation in E2 reactions, for because of steric pressure in the axial conformation of the C–$\overset{+}{N}$ bond, which is the conformation needed for E2 elimination and also perhaps for the ionisation step of the E1 (this latter point will be discussed shortly), the main lability of the system could reside in this bond.

Such compression would cause the bimolecular mechanism to go over easily to the unimolecular by lengthening and polarising the bond to $\overset{\delta+}{C}$—$\overset{\delta+}{N}$, and would thus introduce unsaturation at the α-carbon atom and so stimulate the Saytzeff-controlling influences: thus an E2-reaction from this conformation would possess an E1-like transition state. The isomeric menthyl compound does not undergo unimolecular reactions nearly as easily, although the 'onium group still has to be pushed into an axial conformation for both E1 and E2. This may be due to the lack of an axial hydrogen at C_4 that can assist the ionisation by hyperconjugation with the developing cationic centre.

Entries 1–3 illustrate the non-stereospecificity for the E1 reaction, for elimination can proceed from a carbonium ion into a branch forbidden to the E2 mechanism. It would seem that identical carbonium ions should be formed from the ionisation of menthyl or neomenthyl compounds and so the isomer distribution should be identical in each case, but this is not so, for the neomenthyl ion eliminates to give a super-Saytzeff orientation (entries 7–9)—not the slight preference for this direction as shown by the menthyl compounds which is typical of compounds that obey this rule. These results can best be interpreted if it is assumed that ionisation, as well as bimolecular elimination, can only occur when the α-group occupies an axial orientation (LVII) or (LVIII) and that elimination of a β-hydrogen from the carbonium ion only occurs when the C_β–H bond axis is almost co-planar with the longitudinal axis of the p-orbital on the α-carbon.

(LVII) Neomenthyl   (LVIII) Menthyl   (LIX)

These two requirements are brought about firstly by the necessity for the special orientation of the hydrogen which stabilises a developing centre by hyperconjugation, as has been demonstrated in simpler structures [259]; and secondly for the most efficient intermerging of the disappearing sp^3- and p-orbitals on the β- and α-carbons respectively when they co-alesce to form a π-orbital in the product-forming step. Another factor may be the steric hindrance to solvation of the carbonium ion which develops from the loss of an equatorial group: this would be much less for axial leaving groups.

The ionisation rates of neomenthyl compounds in acetic or formic acids and 80% aqueous ethanol are some 170, 160, and 40-fold greater than those of menthyl compounds, and this has been attributed [257] to this stereo-facilitation of hyperconjugation in the former series which is greater in the acid solvents. Here, ionisation is more difficult (limiting conditions) and requires the maximum intramolecular assistance that it can get. Another factor must be the necessity for forcing all 3 bulky substituents into axial positions to attain the ionising conformation for menthyl compounds, whereas only one group is axial for the neomenthyl isomer. Once the ion is formed, the neomenthyl compound is suitably orientated to eliminate towards C_4 or C_2, and the former mode is predicted by the Saytzeff rule, which is favoured by the rigid geometry to an extent much above that occurring in acyclic compounds. The same influences would also favour a similar direction of elimination from the menthyl ion, but now before a hydrogen atom attached at C_4 could be brought into an axial position, a conformational inversion would have to occur. Such an inversion would be quite rapid, for it would involve the isopropyl group becoming equatorial, but it is not rapid enough to prevent a substantial, although not a major, proportion of the elimination occurring into the other *anti*-Saytzeff branch to give an isomer distribution which is characteristic of that found in straight-chain compounds, in which conformational rotations can readily occur before elimination. The 50-fold difference in the rate of elimination into the Saytzeff-favoured branch for the two isomers seems adequately accounted for by this difference in the structure of the initially produced ions; although neighbouring-group participation to the extent of forming a bridged ion (LIX) has also been suggested. Some hydrogen migration does occur in this reaction (see below), but there seems no necessity to postulate an intermediate or transition state of this sort for these eliminations, for in other instances when such structures have been suggested it seems general that the actual elimination occurs from "classical" carbonium ions, rather than "non-classical" bridged structures [201]. The enhanced solvolysis rate of neomenthyl chloride could also partly be an artefact, caused by bimolecular attack of a solvent molecule on the favourable trans conformation.

Hydride shifts occur under unimolecular conditions and are detected in the study of optically-active menthyl compounds [256]. Such compounds have asymmetric carbon atoms at C_1, C_3 and C_4, and one or both of the last two centres must be destroyed on elimination: but the first is well removed from the reaction sites and can only be affected if at some stage of the process the whole molecule develops an plane of symmetry. In practice it is found that unracemised menth-2-ene is isolated, but that a small fraction of the menth-3-ene is racemised under conditions such that racemisation of the olefin could not have occurred after its for-

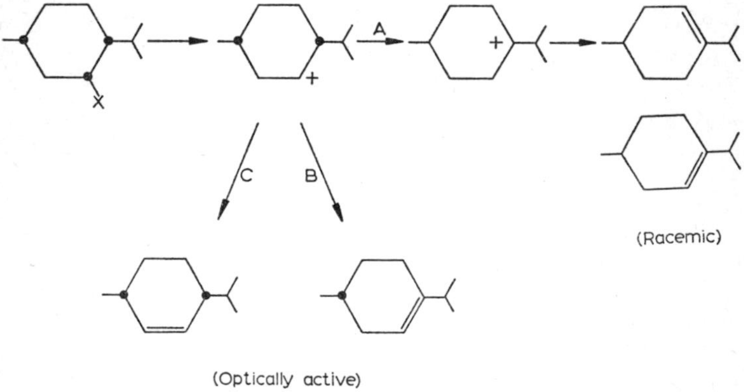

(Racemic)

(Optically active)

>•— indicates an asymmetric carbon atom.   (82)
For neomenthyl chloride A, 14%; B, 81%; C, 1.1%
        menthyl chloride A, 5%; B, 42%; C, 22%

mation. A scheme (82) can account for this, involving a hydride shift from C_4 to C_3 to form a tertiary carbonium ion from a secondary one, but obviously such rearrangements play only a small role, and C_2 to C_3 shifts are not detected. They could be more fully demonstrated by deuterium or ^{14}C labelling.

The olefin proportions and rearrangement tendencies in unimolecular processes will probably depend on the potentialities for ion-association in the manner discussed in Chapter 1; but sufficient work in different solvents with different compounds has not yet been achieved to give experimental illustration to these theories.

(b) Other cyclic systems

Similar studies have been carried out on the *cis*- and *trans*-isomers of (LX) [260] and (LXI) [139] and similar conclusions can be drawn. In these cases there appeared to be no evidence for acceleration of the ionisation of one isomer by β-hydrogen participation of one sort or another, and this can be considered as either

$$CH_2-CH_2$$

$$CH_2 \qquad CHtBu$$

$$CH_2-CHOTS$$

$$CH_2-CH_2$$

$$CH_2 \qquad HCCH_3$$

$$CH_2-CCH_3$$

$$Br$$

$$CH_2-CH_2$$

$$CH_2 \qquad CHCH_3$$

$$CH_2-CHX$$

$$(X = \overset{+}{N}Me_3, OTs)$$

(LX) (LXI) (LXII)

indicative of a lack of a specific bridged-type of participation and of hyperconjugative influences in the aqueous solvents used*, which were very nucleophilic (in comparison with acetic acid) or for (LXI) as showing that steric hindrance to attaining the axial conformations for ionisation was about the same for each isomer.

Recently a study of the decomposition of compounds (LXII) with various bases in several solvents has appeared [114], and the isomer proportions have been interpreted as due to E1 or E2

---

* Under these "non-limiting" conditions, the intramolecular resources for assistance might not be fully developed.

processes: alternative schemes such as merged or α'-β mechanisms cannot be ruled out however.

Some good examples of the stereospecificity of E2 reactions are available for 4-*tert*.-butylcyclohexyl compounds *[261]*, and one series of experiments, which was carried out with potassium *tert*.-butoxide in *tert*.-butanol, gives results as shown in reactions (83)–(85).

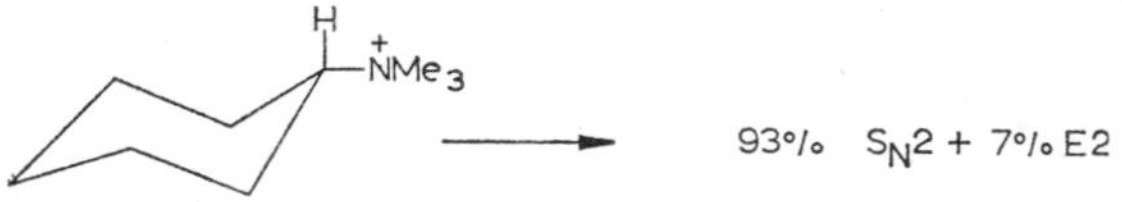

$$93\% \quad S_N2 + 7\% \, E2 \qquad (83)$$

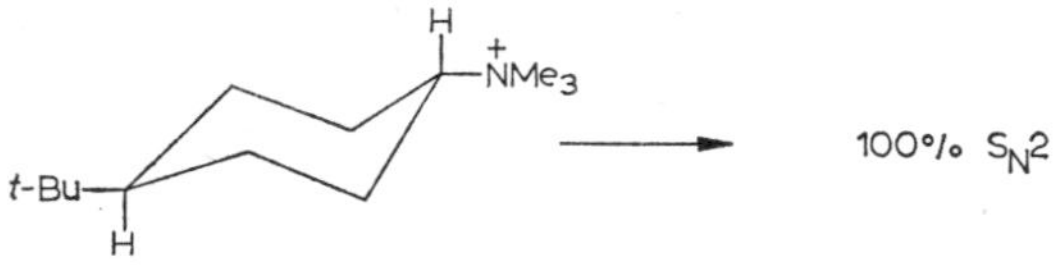

$$100\% \quad S_N2 \qquad (84)$$

trans-Isomer

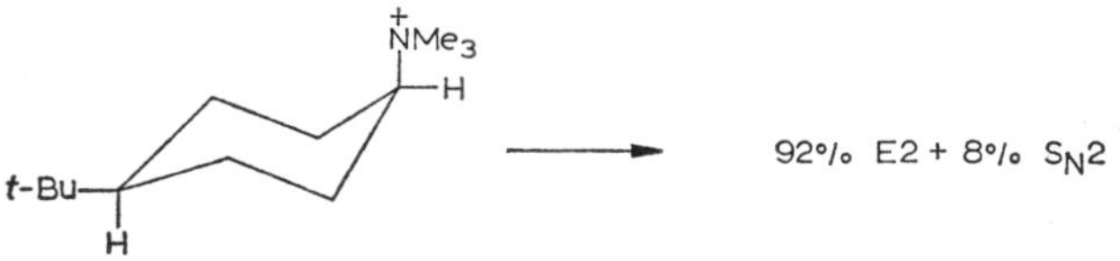

$$92\% \quad E2 + 8\% \, S_N2 \qquad (85)$$

cis-Isomer

The 1-substituent in reaction (83) lies predominantly in an equatorial position and substitution at the methyl groups can occur in this conformation; however, an inversion into an axial conformation appears surprisingly easy and the compound can eliminate from this to the extent of 7% of the total reaction. The substrate of reaction (84) exists with both the substituents equatorial and the energy required to force two such bulky groups into axial positions is too great to allow an elimination to occur, and the stereochemically unrestricted substitution at the methyl groups is allowed to predominate completely. The last compound consists of an equilibrium mixture of conformers in which both the *tert*.-butyl and 'onium groups are axial or equatorial in about the same proportions (the sizes of these two groups are very similar). Reaction of the conformations in which the 'onium group is axial will lead predominantly to elimination, but the observed high olefin yield again indicates that a surprisingly large fraction of the molecules in which this group is equatorial must invert their orientation and undergo elimination, rather than substitution. Interpretation is easier if a less bulky tosylate substituent is considered, for in this case the *tert.*-butyl group will partially fix the conformations by assuming an equatorial position with the other group either axial or equatorial, and there will be considerably different proportions of the conformers than in eqn. (85). The two isomers (LXIII) and (LXIV) react in the way expected *[252]*; and as in this case

(LXIII)

Undergoes $S_N1 + E1$ reaction in presence of NaOEt in EtOH at 75°

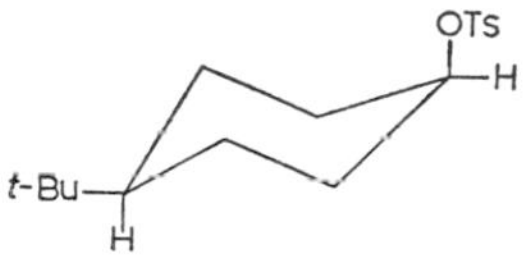

(LXIV)

Readily undergoes E2 reaction in the same conditions

no facile substitution at carbon other than one in the ring can occur, the former example does not undergo bimolecular decomposition since substitution at the C_1 atom as well as elimination are hindered unless the energetically unfavourable inversion can occur, and the competing solvolysis is too rapid for this.

Considerable use has been made of product studies of eliminations to deduce the details of structures of unknown configuration. Thus carvomenthylamine was shown to possess a similar spatial relationship between C_1 and C_2 as menthyl has for C_3 and C_4 by the reaction (86), which leads to one olefin only *[262]*.

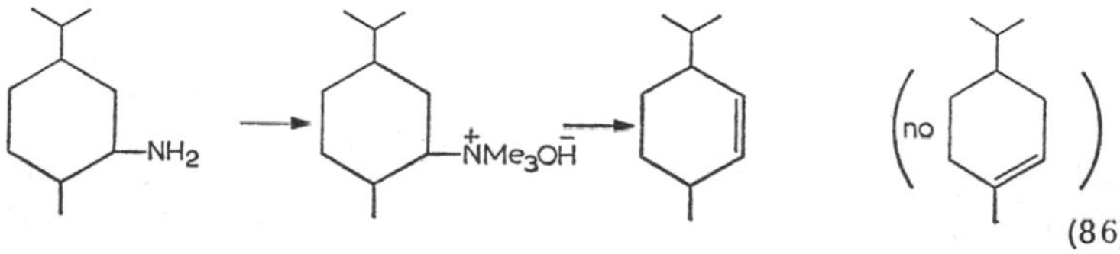

(86)

Analogous product studies have been performed by Hückel in the α- and β-cyclodecalyl series for tosylate and Hofmann degradations and for deaminations [27], but some of the results are difficult to interpret as they stand. A reinvestigation, using modern techniques of characterisation to ensure that pure initial substrates were decomposed in kinetically controlled conditions where no isomer interconversion was possible, would clarify the situation.

(c) Polycyclic systems

Practically all flexibility is removed by *trans*-junctions in multi-fused rings, such as occur in steroids, terpenes, and alkaloids, and the substituents are held rigidly in one conformation. The 3α-epimers (NH_2 axial) of the 5α-cholestane and 5α-pregnane series (LXV) give olefin in excellent yield on degradation, but the 3β-epimers ($-NH_2$ equatorial) give none: only the dimethyl-base is recovered. When, however, a double bond is introduced at the 5-position, *e.g.*

(LXV)   (LXVI)   (LXVII)

(LXVIII)

(LXVI), both epimers readily give olefin [263]: this could be due to a relaxation of the rigidity of the system, to an E1cB mechanism involving the acidic allylic β-hydrogen at the 4-position, or what is most likely to an E1 mechanism promoted trans-annularly by the 5–6 unsaturation.

vic-Dihalides at the C_{11}- and C_{12}-positions in a steroid nucleus (LXVII) are held in very rigid positions, and often trans-substituents will not eliminate on treatment with iodide ion [264]. Apparently these groups both occupy equatorial positions and are unable to flex into the axial conformations.

Some apparent contradictions to the usual rules have been discovered in the series (LXVIII) [265]. The 6α-equatorial amines gave some 5-ene, although the C_5–H is not trans, and the 6β-axial amines underwent Hofmann degradation to give exclusively the 5-enes (with Saytzeff orientation) even though the C_7 possesses a suitably orientated axial hydrogen atom. An explanation involving preliminary stretching of the C_α–$\overset{+}{N}$ bond in the sterically congested transition state elimination (interactions involving the 10-axial methyl group could be important) can be offered as in the neo-menthyl system, or an α'-β mechanism could occur. Kinetic and tracer studies are obviously required. Other examples have been discussed and may be due to similar causes.

When fused systems are linked by cis-junctions, interconversion of the orientation of substituents is usually facile, and restriction on elimination does not occur. For cases where substituents are situated in the body of the fused system, however, interconversion of configuration may be difficult owing to the bulk of the groups to be flexed, even when such substituents are adjacent or near to cis-ring fusions.

4. Larger Ring Systems

Only cis-olefins are known for cyclic systems of seven members or less, for only the conformation (LXIXa) of an olefin precursor can be achieved. Larger, more flexible rings can adopt an orientation (LXXa) and so form a trans-olefin. Hofmann elimination always gives a predominance of the trans-isomer: from the cyclo-octyl, nonyl, and decyl-'onium compounds about 60, 100, and 98% of this product is obtained [266–268], and even when a double bond is already situated in the ring and the system is probably less flexible, this tendency still occurs [269]. The *cis*-isomers are the more stable for all three olefins [266] and so Saytzeff-type influences can have no effect on the stereochemistry of these eliminations. The preference for *trans*-olefin formation must be steric in origin and possibly the

(LXIXa)   *cis*-Olefin   (LXIXb)

(LXXa)   *trans*-Olefin   (LXXb)

trans-Elimination   *cis*-Elimination

the eliminating conformation (LXIXa) allows non-bonded inter-actions between the members of the carbon chain (linked *cis* across the α- and β-carbons) which are absent in the (*trans*-linked) alterna-tive (LXXa). This explanation is supported by the orientation of amine-oxide decompositions, which are believed to require a total eclipsing of the leaving group and the β-hydrogen in the 5-membered cyclic transition state (*cf*. Chap. 7, sect. 3). The lack of flexibility of the cyclo-octyl amine-oxide enables only the conformation (LXIXb) to be utilised and this results in 100% *cis*-olefin formation [226]—the same inflexibility causes a large amount (40%) of *cis*-olefin to be formed from this structure on Hofmann degradation. The less rigid amine-oxides of the cyclononyl and decyl systems can, however, achieve the conformation (LXXb), and so lead to nearly 100% *trans*-olefin [267]. If this explanation is correct, the non-bonded interactions which are present in the initial states cannot be present in the final olefins, since the *cis*-product is more stable and so such interactions must have been relaxed by the change in hybridisation of the carbons from tetrahedral to trigonal.

Olefin formation in a cyclopentyl ring is favoured with respect to that in a cyclohexyl system [270], as is shown by eqn. (87).

$$\text{(87)}$$

This is probably due to some relaxation of bond-eclipsings in the former system when the coordination number of 2 ring-atoms change from 4 to 3. Such a change would increase these non-bonded interactions in the hexyl case, but nevertheless for the 1-methylcycloalkane skeleton the *endo*-1-olefin, which is formed by the introduction of a double bond into the ring, is more stable than the *exo*-isomer in which the double bond involves a methylene group [271, 272]. Elimination from 1-methylcycloalkyl 'onium compounds always gives the less stable olefin (Table 14), as is predicted by the Hofmann rule, except in the one instance [244, 269] of $n = 9$. For the first two entries the elimination probably occurs

TABLE 14

ELIMINATION FROM 1-METHYLCYCLOALKYL COMPOUNDS

n	exo-Olefin	endo-Olefin	
		cis	trans
5	91	9	—*
6	99	1	—*
7	78	22	—*
8	64	37	0
9	48	51	1
10	66	31	2

* Only *cis*-olefin is possible.

into the methyl group in such a predominant fashion because the 'onium group occupies an equatorial conformation in the stable form of the molecule. For the higher homologues the *exo*-proportion falls and passes through a minimum at $n = 9$ when the Saytzeff orientation predominates. The reason for this is presumably that in the more flexible larger rings a larger proportion of the molecules will possess the 'onium group in the axial position, suitable for *endo*-olefin formation, but the reason for the overwhelmingly favourable proportion of the *cis-endo*-olefin in the last entries is less obvious, although an explanation similar to that suggested for the cycloalkyl compounds can be evoked, now allowing for the additional complication of the steric effect of the α-methyl group which would destabilise conformation (LXXa) much more than the alternative (LXIXa).

5. Heterocyclics

The usual rules governing orientation apply to these *[273]* and inspection of the Newman projection (LXXI) of piperidine (which exists in a chair-form similar to cyclohexane) shows that equatorial β-hydrogens are perfectly positioned for elimination accompanying C–N bond fission. The stereochemical situation in the five-membered ring of pyrollidene is not quite so favourable, but double-bond formation is now facilitated by the removal of strain due to non-bonded interactions. Hence the ease of elimination from a 5- and

(LXXI)   (LXXII)   (LXXIII)   (LXXIV)

6-membered aza-ring is very similar; and (LXXII) gives an almost equal mixture of the two possible olefins (*cf.* the situation in eqn. (87) *[270]*). In certain α,α'-disubstituted piperidines, steric hindrance to β-hydrogen abstraction may occur *[274, 275]*.

α-Attached methylene groups will always possess a suitable equatorial hydrogen, but in fused rings a methylene group may not be available. *cis*-Octahydroindole (LXXIII) undergoes C–N fission on Hofmann degradation as shown *[276]*, for this bond can adopt a conformation such that the β- or β'-hydrogens are *trans* with respect to it. The *trans*-isomer (LXXIV) eliminates towards the β"-hydrogen situated in the 5-membered ring *[277]*: the C–N bond is now held rigidly equatorial with respect to the 6-membered ring and no suitably orientated hydrogen exists at β'.

6. Boat-form Alicyclics

An especially interesting group of compounds is those in which a 1,4 or 1,3-bridge across the cyclohexane ring holds the configuration in a strained boat-form and hinders or prevents epimer interconversion. Examples are the bornyl (LXXV), *iso*-bornyl (LXXVI), and pinocamphyl systems (LXXVII).

(LXXV)   (LXXVI)   (LXXVII)

(Only 2- and 3-linked hydrogens are shown in these three formulae)

One restriction to elimination in these structures is summarised by Bredt's rule, which states the impossibility of forming a double bond at a bridgehead carbon atom *[278]*. Thus (LXXVIII) will only eliminate towards the starred carbon atom, and (LXXIX) is extremely resistant to both elimination and substitution by uni- or bi-molecular mechanisms, although some olefin (which may be rearranged) is sluggishly formed with reagents such as $AlBr_3$, $ZnCl_2$, or Ag *[279]*. The theoretical explanation of this rule is that the rigid cage-like structures which are involved in the lower bicyclic compounds do not permit the two C–C bonds linked at the 1-position to become co-planar with the rest of the olefin system, but such a factor might not completely inhibit olefin formation since cyclopropene (LXXX) exists[*], despite very large distortion

(LXXVIII)   (LXXIX)   (LXXX)

(LXXXI)   (LXXXII)

of bond angles (admittedly in one plane). An additional factor discouraging E2 olefin formation is the inability of an equatorial C_1-substituent to become axial, and the E1 mechanism would also be retarded by the difficulty of forming a planar carbonium ion at the bridgehead, although this difficulty can apparently be overcome by the Lewis acids mentioned in connection with (LXXIX). As the ring size increases, any strain in the products is distributed over a larger number of bond junctions and the rule is relaxed: possibly one of the simplest structures for which the rule is broken is the bicyclononene (LXXXI), and double bonds are readily formed towards bridgeheads in the decalin series (LXXXII).

In boat structures, the four groups attached to the 2- and 3-positions are held in eclipsed positions, see (LXXVI), in two planes which intersect at about 60°. For the 2-substituted 1,4-bridged structures elimination cannot occur towards C_1 because of Bredt's rule and a trans-planar elimination transition state towards C_3 cannot be achieved without considerable strain which would be strongly resisted by the buttressing effect of the trans-

---

[*] This olefin can be prepared by the Hofmann degradation of the cyclopropyl 'onium hydroxide or by addition of methylene to acetylene.

annular bridge. However, isobornyl halides with strong alkali in water at 150°, or with 10% sodium pentoxide in *n*-pentanol at 190° (poorly ionising conditions), do give the 2,3-olefin (bornylene) in good yield, as does the decomposition of the 'onium salt on pyrolysis, but not in basic solution (see p. 111). Under the last mentioned conditions almost complete substitution and elimination with rearrangement occurs. Forcing E2 conditions might cause *cis* or *trans* one-step processes to occur against the unfavourable geometry, but also the situation would seem very suitable for the appearance of E1cB, α, and (for the 'onium compounds) α'-β mechanisms. Full kinetic analyses with halides and 'onium compounds containing deuterium should demonstrate the occurrence of these.

Except under these extreme bimolecular conditions, ionisation and rearrangement is the mode for these compounds for by such means the strain is relieved. The best known examples are the bornyl-isobornyl to camphene conversions formulated in eqn. (78) where thermodynamic control operates to give the product mixtures. The timing of these changes, and the nature of the ions involved, whether "open-classical" or "bridged non-classical", will not be considered here: the problem is complex and has been the subject of several kinetic and tracer studies [25].

Several other boat structures have been studied. The bimolecular eliminations of the *cis*- and *trans*-2,3-dichloro, 2-tosyl-3-chloro, and 2-chloro-3-phenylsulphone compounds of norbornane (the skeleton of which is (LXXXIII)) have been kinetically analysed and were

(LXXXIII)   (LXXXIV)   (LXXXV)

concluded to proceed by two-step E1cB processes [280]; but tracer studies and experiments to detect general base catalysis are lacking, and so the limits of such processes cannot be delineated. Similar deductions have been recorded concerning reactions of the structures (LXXXIV), and in both of these types the *exo*-amine on Hofmann degradation gave much more olefin than the *endo* [281]. Brief studies, with no mechanistic conclusion, have shown that *endo*-'onium compounds (LXXXV) also can readily eliminate to the 2-olefin, both under Hofmann conditions, and with phenyllithium in ether when a ylide intermediate can be isolated [282]. Compounds of the type (LXXXVI), with the bridge substituted

(LXXXVI)
(X=Cl, X'=C$_7$H$_7$SO$_2$)

(LXXXVII)

(LXXXVIII)

both *cis* and *trans*, have been decomposed and the great ease of elimination in both cases (*cf.* the dichlorobornanes) and lack of stereospecificity when one substituent was a sulphone group, indicated that a two-step mechanism occurred [283]. The decomposition of both *cis*- and *trans*-dichloro-compounds [33] was slower (owing to a free energy of activation greater by 4–8 kcal.-mole^{-1}) than the rate under comparable conditions for those isomers of benzene hexachloride which allow direct trans-planar elimination, and this difference can be attributed to the difficulty of achieving this preferred geometry when a bicyclic ring is present. However the most surprising discovery about this system was that the isomer which underwent overall *cis*-elimination did so about 8 times as fast as the other which could pursue *trans*-elimination albeit with some constraint. Detailed analysis showed that the latter reaction had an activation energy about 4 kcal.mole^{-1} more favourable than the other (the smallness of the difference compared with the 10–12 kcal.mole^{-1} found in the benzene hexachlorides is due to the greater ease of attaining the trans-planar conformation in this more flexible system) but that the entropy factor favoured overall *cis*-elimination by a quantity which outweighed this, and so this latter factor controlled the actual rate. In cyclohexane rings, the energy difference between the *trans*- and *cis*-processes is much too large ever to be counterbalanced, let alone outweighed.

The *cis*-disubstituted acenaphthenes (LXXXVII) reacted some 750 times faster than the *trans*-isomers [284], and this indicates that concerted *trans*-elimination here occurs, for the bridge is not held as rigidly as in the bicycloheptane and octane types and considerable rotation is possible about the C_1–C_2 bond. The situation is much more extreme for the disubstituted dihydrophenanthrenes (LXXXVIII) in which the 6-membered ring including the two tetrahedral carbon atoms has a flexibility tempered by the tendency of the diphenyl structure to become planar. Here elimination from the *trans*-isomer was more restricted than that from β-benzene hexachloride [285].

There are several reports in the terpene field that eliminations from 'onium salts do not proceed in the expected direction. The pinocamphyl salt (LXXXIX) gives mainly α-pinene (XC) [286] and the thujyl 'onium compound (XCI) also gives the non-Hofmann product in major yield [287]. The configurations of these reactants

(LXXXIX)   (XC)   (XCI)

are uncertain and probably a mixture of isomers was used in these experiments, but these orientations of elimination are difficult to explain on any stereochemical, steric, or polar basis for any particular isomer. It is possible that the ease of formation of a non-classical carbonium ion in these cases could result in an E1, rather than an E2, process even under the pyrolytic conditions of a Hofmann Degradation, and so lead to Saytzeff-type orientation of decomposition. Such a mechanism seems reasonable for (XCI), for a "tris-homocyclopropenyl ion", as represented above, could be formed which is similar to the species which have been identified as reaction intermediates in closely related types of systems [288].

Chapter 6

OTHER ELIMINATION PROCESSES

The mechanisms of several other classes of eliminations, some of which are of synthetic importance, have been studied. The main interest of these is the elucidation of the number and nature of the reaction steps, for no new basic processes are involved.

1. Metal-promoted Eliminations

Several types of reaction involve the β-elimination of halogen and another group and are initiated by zinc or magnesium in protic media, particularly acetic acid. The general scheme is eqn. (88)

$$M + RCHYCHR'X \longrightarrow RCH{:}CHR' + \overset{++}{M} + \bar{X} + \bar{Y} \qquad (88)$$

where Y is $\cdot$Hal, X is $\cdot$Hal, $\cdot$OR, $\cdot$OCOR or $\cdot$OH, and M is the metal. Such processes are heterogeneous and have rarely been studied kinetically, but they are useful; for when carried out under conditions not allowing prototropic shifts they can form only one olefin (excluding elimination from diastereoisomers).

The best studied of these reactions is the dehalogenation of *vic*-dihalides with zinc, which works well with all combinations of halogens except those including fluorine, and which is familiar as the regenerative step in the purification of olefins via their dibromides. A carbonium ion mechanism, requiring electrophilic catalysis, can be excluded because products of substitution and dehydrohalogenation are never found, and a carbanion intermediate as in eqn. (89) is almost certainly involved *[30]*. This must

$$Zn + X{-}\overset{\displaystyle |}{\underset{\displaystyle |}{C}}{-}\overset{\displaystyle |}{\underset{\displaystyle |}{C}}{-}X \longrightarrow {-}\overset{\ominus}{\underset{\displaystyle |}{C}}{-}\overset{\displaystyle |}{\underset{\displaystyle |}{C}}{-}X \longrightarrow \overset{\displaystyle |}{\underset{\displaystyle |}{C}}{:}\overset{\displaystyle |}{\underset{\displaystyle |}{C}} + \bar{X} \qquad (89)$$

have a transient existence for no product of interaction with the solvent has ever been isolated, and it is likely that the ion is bonded in some way to the metal surface—just as carbonium ions are believed to be absorbed on alumina catalysts (*cf.* sect. 5). A two-stage, rather than a synchronous E2, process is indicated by product studies on homologous *vic*-dibromides. *meso*-Dideuterodibromo-ethane (XCII) and the diastereoisomeric 2,3-dibromobutanes (XCIII) on reaction with zinc gave only the *cis*- or *trans*-olefins

(XCII)   (XCIII)

that are expected from trans-E2 processes *[289]*; but the most favoured initial conformations of these compounds, which are controlled by steric and polar factors, are as shown, and a carbanion formed from any of these orientations and which rapidly decomposed would give these products. Such stereospecificity was not maintained for higher homologues, and if a particular stereoisomer of the dibromo-pentanes, -hexanes, or -octanes was debrominated and the halogen re-added to the olefinic product, it was found that 3, 6, and 20% of the other isomer was obtained in addition to the original starting material *[290]*. If the re-addition of bromine was entirely *trans**, this means that some *cis*-elimination occurred in the debromination step and the product distribution can be best interpreted in terms of a carbanion process in which the large α- and β-linked groups cause the ground state of the substrate to possess increasing proportions of conformations other than that in which the two leaving groups are *trans* and co-planar. A carbanion formed from such initial geometries could invert and decompose to give overall *cis*-elimination before it could react with the solvent

---

* Despite the widespread conviction that *trans*-addition of halogens to double bonds always occurs, there is little supporting evidence for the complete stereospecificity of this mechanism.

or rotate into a conformation for *trans*-elimination. Stereospecificity is completely lost when substituents such as COOR or Ph are present *[290, 291]*, due both to steric factors controlling the populations of the conformations and more importantly to the longer-life of the now stabilised carbanion.

Similar reactions and mechanisms occur with magnesium *[289]*; as is shown by the intrusion of elimination and cyclisation when attempts are made to prepare Grignard reagents from 1,2- and 1,3-dihalides respectively. The function of the solvent in all these reactions is probably to remove halide salt from the reactive surfaces of the metal; although, especially in non-polar media, catalysis by the metal halide which accumulates during the reaction has been detected *[292]*.

An alternative view *[291]* of these reactions is that an organo-metallic compound (*e.g.* $BrZnCR_2CR_2Br$) is formed, presumably through the mediation of a carbanion, and this then breaks down with synchronous loss of the two fragments from the α- and β-atoms. However, some reaction with the solvent, either at the carbanion or final organo-metallic stages would surely here be expected. There is considerable evidence that radical processes forming *e.g.* $\cdot CR_2CR_2X$, are unimportant *[291]*.

Halo-hydrins and related compounds apparently form a carbanion which has less tendency to decompose than in the above cases, and so is stable enough to give non-stereospecific elimination without however being long-lived enough to react with the solvent. On reaction with zinc, a similar olefin mixture (usually with a preponderance of the more stable *trans*-isomer) was formed at the same rate from each pair of diastereoisomers in acyclic *[291]*, cyclohexyl *[293, 294]*, and steroid *[295]* compounds under conditions where no isomerisation of reactants or products was possible. It is significant that zinc cannot remove HOCl from chlorohydrins (in the few cases that have been studied) although the corresponding acid can be eliminated from bromo- and iodo-hydrins and chlorine can be removed from *vic*-dihalides. Another mechanism has been proposed *[296]* for halo-hydrins which is based on the observation that such eliminations have usually been carried out in acidic media (typically AcOH or AcOH–HCl) and a process (90) has been suggested which would favour *trans*-elimination but was considered relatively unsuitable for chlorohydrins because of the difficulty of

$$
\begin{array}{ccc}
\underset{\displaystyle |\ \ |}{\overset{\displaystyle \text{OH}}{-\text{C}-\text{C}-}} & \xrightarrow{\ \overset{+}{\text{H}}\ } & \underset{\displaystyle |\ \ |}{\overset{\displaystyle \overset{+}{\text{O}}\text{H}_2}{-\text{C}-\text{C}-}} \longrightarrow -\text{C}\underset{\underset{\oplus}{\diagdown\text{I}\diagup}}{\qquad}\text{C}- \xrightarrow[\text{Zn, MCl}_2,\ \text{MCl}_3]{\text{reagent}} \diagup\!\!\!\diagdown\text{C}=\text{C}\diagup\!\!\!\diagdown \qquad (90)
\end{array}
$$

forming the chloronium ion as a configuration-holding intermediate. Complete non-stereospecificity must occur for zinc, but with chromous and stannous chlorides in aqueous AcOH–HCl, about 75 and 100 % *trans*-elimination occurred and complete *trans*-specificity was also achieved if a non-protonic mixture of $POCl_3$ in pyridine (which is known to dehydrate alcohols to olefins) was used in conjunction with stannous chloride. Such a mechanism might be extended to the ferrous and chromous chloride-catalysed eliminations from *vic*-dihalides [297]*.

Alkali-metals in liquid ammonia, tetrahydrofuran, or other inert solvents will also dehalogenate these compounds (both *vic*-dihalides and others) with complete non-stereospecificity [289, 290]. These may be radical processes similar to those that may occur in Würtz-type reactions of mono-halides, eqn. (91), but carbanions could

$$
-\text{C}-\text{C}-\text{X} \xrightarrow{\ \text{Na}\ } -\text{C}-\text{C}-\text{C}-\text{C}- + \ \diagdown\text{C}=\text{C}\diagup + -\text{C}-\text{C}=\text{C}-\text{C}- \qquad (91)
$$

also be formed by radical formation followed by electron capture; especially in such a rich electron source as a solution of a metal in liquid ammonia. The relative importance of ionic and radical processes in Würtz reactions is disputed; but the former probably play the major part although α-elimination of HX to form carbenes R_2C: may also occur. Presumably dehalogenations follow paths

* This mechanism cannot occur in all cases: for instance; the dehydroxybromination of 3-bromo-borneol with zinc in ethanol yields only bornylene [298]. A carbonium-ion mechanism would lead to bromocamphene.

similar to those previously discussed (Chap. 4, sect. 3), and electron-spin resonance studies of reacting mixtures could prove fruitful.

2. Dehalogenation with Iodide Ion

This is a well-known method as applied to *vic*-dihalides, especially bromides, and the elimination is irreversible as the iodine halide produced is destroyed by the reagent. The decompositions of the isomeric 2,3-dibromobutanes are almost entirely *trans*-specific [30], and it is believed that in this case the iodide ion attacks the halogen atom in a manner analogous to the attack of a base on a β-hydrogen in synchronous dehydrohalogenations, eqn. (92). Carbanion mecha-

$$\overset{\frown}{I^-} \; BrCHCH_3CHCH_3Br \longrightarrow IBr + CH_3CH:CHCH_3 + \bar{Br} \qquad (92)$$

nisms would seem less likely in these homogeneous conditions. The double bond must be well-developed in the transition state, for the eclipsing effect of the α- and β-methyl groups in the example shown above causes a difference of about 6-fold in the rates of formation of the *cis*- and *trans*-olefins, which is close to the value expected if all the free energy difference between the final products were exhibited in this state. In certain types of structures a 2,3-rearrangement can occur during the elimination [299].

Iodide ion is highly nucleophilic towards carbon in protic media, and the dehalogenation of ethylene dibromide has been shown to involve a rate-determining S_N2 attack to form an iodobromo compound which subsequently decomposes, perhaps as a result of

$$\bar{I} + BrCH_2CH_2Br \xrightarrow{\text{slow}} ICH_2CH_2Br \xrightarrow[\bar{I}]{\text{fast}}$$

$$\left[\begin{array}{c} CH_2\text{---}CH_2 \\ \diagdown I_2 \diagup \end{array} \right]_? \xrightarrow{\text{fast}} CH_2:CH_2 \qquad\qquad (93)$$

further iodide attack, eqn. (93). This mechanism is supported by rate data [300] and is elegantly demonstrated by the observation of complete overall *cis*-elimination from the *meso*-dideutero compound, eqn. (94) *[289b]*.

A similar mechanism occurs for 1,2-dibromopropane and 1,2-dibromobutane, but is unimportant, although detectable, for 2,3-dibromobutane; and this difference is presumably due to the steric hindrance to attack at the secondary carbon in the last case which reduces the substitution rate well below that of the synchronous elimination. *Trans*-elimination is favoured over *cis*-elimination from 1,2-cyclohexyl and steroid structures by factors of 10–70 (for these compounds zinc shows no discrimination) and the *cis* processes undoubtedly occur through preliminary substitution and inversion of configuration *[294, 295, 301, 302]*.

Replacement of sulphonate groups can be achieved similarly by S_N2 processes to give unstable mono- or di-iodo compounds and the subsequent introduction of unsaturation, which has been particularly studied for the ditosylates of alicyclics, carbohydrates, and steroids, involves the inversion of configuration at one or at both of the carbon atoms, eqn. (95), and produces an intermediate that has been isolated in some cases *[108, 301, 303]*. Carbanion mechanisms have also been proposed for these processes but on inadequate evidence.

These dehalogenations are sometimes carried out in a solvent, such as acetone, which enhances the nucleophilicity of the reagent towards carbon (and presumably towards halogens also) and a standard method for polyhalides uses MgI_2 in ether. It would be interesting to observe if eliminations via the synchronous E2 process could be achieved with other ions, particularly other halides, in dipolar aprotic solvents.

3. Acetylene Formation

Strong bases readily dehydrohalogenate *vic-* or *gem-*dihalides to give alkynes, which if non-terminal will often rearrange to the more stable 1-isomer, probably through allene formation. The first elimination step gives a halo-alkene which is relatively stable, but treatment with alcoholic alkali or sodamide in xylene in sealed tubes at above 100°, or often at reflux temperatures, will cause the loss of a second molecule of hydrogen halide. There is less tendency for isomerisation with the former reagent [304].

The groups involved in elimination from an alkene are held in co-planar positions, uncomplicated by any conformational problems,

TABLE 15

RELATIVE RATES OF *cis-*AND *trans-*ELIMINATIONS

Compound	trans/cis[*]	Δ(ΔG)[**]	Ref.
PhCH:CHBr	210,000	7.4	[305]
p-$NO_2C_6H_4$CH:CHBr	16,000	5.9	[305]
HalCH:CHHal	10,000–1,000	4–5	[306]
$CO\overline{O}$CCl:CHCO$\overline{O}$	10–50	1.4–2.4	[307, 308]
$CO\overline{O}$CBr:CHCO$\overline{O}$	17	1.7	[307]
CH_3CH:CHBr	7	1.2	[309]

[*] Ratio of the *trans-* and *cis-*elimination rates (of H–Hal) from the *cis-* and *trans-*isomers respectively
[**] Difference of free energy of activation for *cis-* and *trans-*isomers (kcal.mole⁻¹).

and it is found that *trans*-elimination (from a *cis*-substituted olefin (XCIV)) is favoured over *cis*-elimination (from the *trans*-isomer (XCV)). Some rates for dehydrohalogenations promoted by alkoxides in aqueous media are given in Table 15, and a better idea of the relative facilities is gathered from the differences of free energies of activation for the two isomers. Similar trends are found when two halogen atoms are removed with Zn or when CO_2 and a halogen are lost [310] (XCVI), but dehalogenation with iodide ion has not yet been systematically studied.

(XCIV)   (XCV)   (XCVI)   (XCVII)   (XCVIII)

It was a qualitative appreciation of such reactivity differences that caused the general recognition of *trans*-elimination in base-catalysed reactions before kinetic or product studies had been carried out on saturated compounds [26]. A well-known example outside the field of dehydrohalogenations is the much greater ease of the base-promoted formation of nitriles from *anti*-aldoxime acetates (XCVIII) than from the *syn*-isomers.

The reactivity differences between the first two compounds cited are of the order of those obtained for benzene hexachlorides and are much larger than those recorded in the cyclic systems discussed in Chap. 4, sect. 2. Cristol proposed [305a] that *trans*-elimination in these cases was synchronous but that *cis*-elimination (from the *trans*-isomers) involved a two-step E1cB process, which was favoured by the stabilisation of the anion by structures such as (XCVII) when a *p*-nitrophenyl substituent was present. Although phenyl groups can so stabilise a carbanion in saturated alkyl systems, a large fraction of the resonance energy of the initial state must be lost when a carbanion is formed in these unsaturated systems and the conjugation between the aryl group and the double bond is partially destroyed. Another factor tending to increase the ratio of the *trans*- and *cis*-rates would be the release of steric strain between the rigidly held *cis*-aryl and bromine groups on entering the transition state for *trans*-elimination. Such conjugative effects, and such steric-accelerations are much smaller in the other examples quoted and consequently the differences of reactivity between the isomers are much less than in the first two examples. Not all of the later cases have been carefully studied with respect to products, and the last example may involve isomer inter-conversion either before or during reaction, for *cis-trans* isomeri-sation of the substrate occurs at room temperature on exposure to light, probably due to catalysis by the traces of molecular bromine formed. The fourth and fifth examples in Table 15 are interesting because *trans*-elimination is preferred even though electrostatic repulsion between the two negatively-charged sub-stituents and the anionic reagent would be much greater for this orientation of elimination than for the alternative. The *trans-cis* ratios are, however, low; and carbanion formation is probably facilitated in these cases by such substituents; just as it is favoured in the saturated dihalo-malic and succinic acids *[197]*. A de-carboxylation (XCVI) rather than a dehydrohalogenation can occur for the *trans*-isomer at low basicities *[310–312]*, and analogous reactions occur from bromocinnamic acids *[472]*.

cis-Elimination is twice as fast as *trans* for PhCH:CHBr (*cf.* Table 15) in non-polar aprotic media with strong bases (*e.g.* PhLi in ether) and this can be accommodated in terms of a cyclic transition state (XCIX) in the former case in solvents which favour

(XCIX)

ion-pairing *[209]*; but the *cis*-isomer would have to react via *trans*-elimination as before. An α-elimination mechanism is possible for both isomers *[215]*.

4. Dehydration of Alcohols

This is a classical preparative method for olefins, and the usual procedure is to heat the substrate with a Brønsted acid or a Lewis acid such as $ZnCl_2$ or I_2. Two distinct types of reaction are involved. When a strong mineral or organic acid is used, the alcohol is protonated and breaks down in an El reaction (96): there is no evidence that the species $R\overset{+}{O}H_2$ can undergo E2 decomposition with the solvent or with the anion of the acid. A similar mechanism (97)

$$ROH \underset{\text{fast}}{\overset{\overset{+}{H}}{\rightleftharpoons}} R\overset{+}{O}H_2 \xrightarrow{\text{slow}} \overset{+}{R} \xrightarrow{\text{fast}} \text{Olefin} \qquad (96)$$

$$ROH \xrightarrow[\text{fast}]{I_2} RO\overset{+}{H}I \xrightarrow{\text{slow}} \overset{+}{R} \xrightarrow{\text{fast}} \text{Olefin} \qquad (97)$$

also occurs in the Hibbert reaction [313] whereby tertiary and some secondary alcohols are dehydrated by heating with traces of iodine. Certain acids (e.g. H_2SO_4, sulphonic, oxalic), anhydrides (e.g. boric, phthalic, acetic), and other reagents (e.g. $POCl_3$ in pyridine, P_2O_5 in xylene) may also form esters which subsequently decompose either thermally or by El or E2 pathways, especially on refluxing in high-boiling solvents. Only when an alcohol possesses a β-hydrogen that is activated by carbonyl groups or double bonds can direct dehydration by bases be achieved [314, 315].

(a) Dehydration by means of strong acids

The olefins produced by these reactions are generally those predicted by the Saytzeff rule, but this cannot be taken as evidence for a carbonium-ion mechanism because under the reaction conditions isomerisation would usually occur to give thermodynamic rather than kinetic control of the products. However, other evidence for an El process is strong [316]: the order of reactivity is tertiary alcohols > secondary > primary, which is the order of ease of ion formation, and skeletal rearrangement occurs in compounds which would give carbonium ions known to be disposed for this. For the Hibbert reaction, the tendency for elimination is favoured by

β-substituents in the order $Me > Et > i\text{-}Pr > H$, and the proportions of isomers from the decomposition of *tert*-amyl alcohol is the same as that obtained from *tert*-amyl halides and 'onium compounds under E1 conditions. The acid-catalysed decomposition of ethers shows the same trends and probably proceeds through the ionisation of the protonated substrate $R\overset{+}{O}HR'$: in this case the Hibbert method cannot be used.

The decomposition involving iodine is useful because the weakly acidic conditions do not cause isomerisation of products or of sensitive substrates. An example is the dehydration of linalool (C) which with acids gives cyclic products, (perhaps partly due to

(C)   (CI)   (CII)

prior conversion to geraniol (CI)), but with iodine gives predominantly the unrearranged Saytzeff product (CII).

The details of these E1 processes have been studied by Taft and Dostovsky and their co-workers. The rates of olefin formation from *n*- [317], *sec*- [318, 319], and *tert*-butanol [320] and α-phenylethanol [321] were smaller than the rates of acid-catalysed oxygen exchange with $H_2^{18}O$ and were best interpreted by a scheme (98). For the tertiary and secondary alcohols, oxygen exchange occurred via the reverse of the second step, but for primaries a synchronous process (99) was utilised. An elimination mechanism (100), which would also lead to exchange, was excluded in all cases. Evidence for a carbonium-ion process was that the activation energy of step 1

$$ROH \rightleftharpoons R\overset{+}{O}H_2 \underset{-1}{\overset{1}{\rightleftharpoons}} \overset{+}{R} \text{ (solvated)} \xrightarrow{\;2\;} \text{Olefin} \qquad (98)$$

$$H_2^{18}O + R\overset{+}{O}H_2 \rightleftharpoons R^{18}\overset{+}{O}H_2 + H_2O \qquad (99)$$

$$H_2O + R\overset{+}{O}H_2 \rightleftharpoons H_3\overset{+}{O} + \text{olefin} + H_2O \qquad (100)$$

for *tert*-butanol was *ca.* 30 kcal.mole^{-1}, and the difference between that of steps 2 and —1 and the value of k_2/k_{-1} were nearly identical with those values deduced for the E1 decompositions of *tert*-butyl cations from other sources. The unimportance of E2 mechanisms involving $R\overset{+}{O}H_2$ is probably due to the lack of a suitable base in the aqueous acidic media, and so the relatively fast ionisation, for which the large positive entropy of activation over-rides the large activation energy, predominated.

Attempts have been made to determine the nature of the fast steps following the heterolysis; in particular by the study of the reverse reaction—the acid-catalysed hydration of olefins—and the use of the principle of microscopic reversibility (*cf.* Chap. 1, sect. 1c). An elegant investigation of the isomerisations, dehydrations, exchanges, and hydrations associated with the action of acid on *sec*-butanol was interpreted on the basis of an intermediate carbonium ion, common to all these processes, which was partially bonded to one molecule of water on either side of its plane *[318]*.

The dependence of the rate of hydration (in aqueous acids) of several olefins on the h_0 acidity function and the lack of uptake of deuterium tracer from the solvent by unreacted olefin led to the scheme (101) for the reverse reaction in which "fast" and

$$-\overset{|}{\underset{|}{C}}-\overset{|}{\underset{|}{C}}-OH \underset{f}{\overset{f}{\rightleftharpoons}} -\overset{|}{\underset{|}{C}}-\overset{|}{\underset{|}{C}}-\overset{+}{O}H_2 \underset{f}{\overset{s}{\rightleftharpoons}} -\overset{|}{\underset{|}{C}}-\overset{|}{\underset{|}{C}}{}^+ \underset{s}{\overset{s}{\rightleftharpoons}}$$

$$\boxed{\underset{/}{\overset{\diagdown}{C}}=\overset{H^+}{\overset{|}{\underset{/}{C}}}\diagdown} \underset{f}{\overset{f}{\rightleftharpoons}} \underset{/}{\overset{\diagdown}{C}}-\overset{\diagdown}{\underset{/}{C}} + H_3\overset{+}{O} \quad (101)$$

(f = fast, s = slow)

(CIII)

"slow" refer to the magnitudes of the rate constants *[322, 323]:* If the relative material-transfers per unit-time are considered, a different designation of the steps is necessary *[323]*. An intermediate "π-complex" (CIII), such that the proton was not directly lost from the β-carbon atom to the solvent but was first transferred to the π-orbital of the developing double-bond, was introduced into this scheme in order to account for the acid dependence, for it was supposed that the rate of hydration would become dependent on $(H_3\overset{+}{O})$ rather than on h_0 if that part of the mechanism enclosed in the box were removed. The original reasoning was fallacious and now it is believed that slow proton-transfers would be dependent on h_0 [324]; but nevertheless recent detailed studies by Taft [323] on the acidity and temperature dependence of the rate of ^{18}O exchange, dehydration, and hydration of tertiary alcohols in aqueous acids have been interpreted as evidence for π-complex formation. These rates were all dependent on h_0, and this indicated that the activity coefficients of the transition states of the rate-determining processes closely resembled that of an oxonium ion rather than a carbonium ion, for if a "free" carbonium ion such as pictured in eqn. (98) was formed, a dependence on the j_0 acidity function would have been expected. This qualification is reasonable, for relatively unsolvated "hot" (cf. sect. 6) carbonium ions are unlikely to be formed from these heterolyses in aqueous media. Two mechanisms were consistent with the kinetic data: one similar to eqn. (101) involving an "encumbered ion" which was shielded by the leaving water molecule (i.e. $\overset{+}{R} \ldots OH_2$) and which corresponded to the intimate ion-pair formed if both fragments were ionic; and a second, similar to eqn. (98), involving a solvated but otherwise free ion which possessed the above-mentioned activity-coefficient qualification. The former scheme was preferred, and was held to accommodate recent observations on the non-stereospecific addition of water to tertiary olefins in aqueous acid. (The addition of HCl to similar olefins in aprotic media was trans-stereospecific)* [325].

A similar intermediate π-complex was supposed to account for the large preference for cis-but-2-ene (rather than the more stable trans-isomer) which was found in the dehydration of sec-butanol by acids and solid catalysts [318]. The pathway to the cis-isomer was believed to be facilitated by analogy with the greater stability

---

* Views differing from those of Taft have been recently expressed [326].

of the coordination-compounds formed by certain Lewis acids with
cis- than with trans-olefins, but the differences in size, availability
of orbitals, and electron affinities between $\overset{+}{H}$ and a typical Lewis
acid such as $\overset{+}{Ag}$ makes the parallel rather tenuous and the reasons
for this isomer-distribution are obscure. It is significant that proton
loss in other E1 processes, which would be expected to proceed via
the same intermediates, does not lead to an abnormal ratio of
geometrical isomers. π-Complexes have been postulated in many
mechanistic schemes on dubious experimental and theoretical
grounds [327], but their identification with reaction intermediates
which have no unique kinetic consequences and which cannot be
partitioned or diverted must be viewed with reserve. Apparently
a distinction must be made between these complexes and the
hydrogen-bridged intermediates which have been postulated for
hydride-shift in carbonium ions; for whereas the former are alleged
to rapidly equilibrate with a deuterated solvent, it is found that
tracer is not picked up from the medium in the rearrangements
accompanying diazotisation (cf. sect. 6) [328].

It has been suggested [319] that the proton is ultimately transferred to the solvent shell rather than to a specific water molecule,
for the rate of elimination is independent of the activity of water
in an acid solution (unlike the exchange of $H_2{}^{18}O$). Such a distinction
may not be clear cut insomuch as any solvent molecule is, in some
degree, part of a larger hydrogen-bonded structure and the concept
is not in accord with the hydrogen-bonded or diffusion-controlled
models for E1 proton-loss that were previously discussed (Chap. 1,
sect. 1c); although it seems compatible with proton-transfer to the
water molecule which is involved in an encumbered carbonium ion.

(b) Other dehydration mechanisms

Sulphuric and phosphoric acids, potassium hydrogen sulphate,
and the Lewis acids previously mentioned can form esters which
could be intermediates in the dehydration process; and for sulphuric
acid the formation of an ester $ROSO_2OH$ is well established in
the "continuous process" for the production of ethers with olefin
formation as a by-product. Information concerning such reactions

is entirely qualitative and much confused, but (for the stronger acids) ester and oxonium ion formation and subsequent uni- or bi-molecular decomposition probably occur simultaneously or within different ranges of conditions with different substrates. The obvious approach of studying the decomposition of the separately-prepared esters under dehydration conditions does not seem to have been adopted: indeed the effect of different dehydrating agents on simple acyclic alcohols has not been studied systematically, and most information pertains to fragmentary observations with more complicated cyclic structures.

Carbonium ion processes undoubtedly occur in many cases and can be identified when rearrangement is detected, as in eqn. (102)

$$
\begin{array}{c}
\quad\quad\quad\text{C} \\
\quad\quad\quad| \\
\text{C}\quad\text{C} \\
|\quad\,| \\
\text{C}-\text{C}-\text{C}-\text{C}-\text{C} \\
|\quad\,| \\
\text{C}\quad\text{OH}
\end{array}
\xrightarrow[\text{acid}]{\beta\text{-naphthyl sulphonic}}
\begin{array}{c}
\begin{array}{c}
\quad\quad\quad\text{C} \\
\quad\quad\quad| \\
\text{C}\quad\text{C} \\
|\quad\,| \\
\text{C}-\text{C}-\text{C}=\text{C}-\text{C} \quad (58\%)\\
|\\
\text{C}
\end{array}\\[2em]
\begin{array}{c}
\quad\quad\quad\text{C}\\
\quad\quad\quad|\\
\text{C}\quad\text{C}\\
|\quad\,|\quad\,\,\,\text{C}\\
\text{C}-\text{C}-\text{C}=\text{C}\diagup \quad (42\%)\\
\quad\quad\quad\quad\diagdown\text{C}
\end{array}
\end{array}
\qquad (102)
$$

which must involve 1,3-methyl shifts [329]*; but the progenitor of the ion may be either an oxonium ion or an ester. Sulphonate groups very easily split-off to leave carbonium ions, but E1 reactions of other esters can also occur if the alkyl structure possesses a large driving force for ionisation. This is shown by iso-borneol which can form a carbonium ion by synartetically-assisted ionisation when treated with phthalic anhydride, eqn. (103), whereas the endo-isomer—borneol—which cannot evoke such assistance merely gives a stable ester under the same conditions [330]. The formation of an oxonium ion is not possible with this reagent, but

---

* An alternative scheme requires an improbably large number of 1,2-shifts.

when such an ion can be formed, as by treatment of the alcohol with dilute mineral acids, both isomers give rearranged olefins *[331]*. Phthalate esters do not form carbonium ions from more typical

(103)*

structures, and good yields of unrearranged products are formed according to the Saytzeff rule at elevated temperatures from tertiary alcohols which would form carbonium ions that are known to rearrange *[332]*: here ester formation may be followed by a thermal decomposition involving mechanisms that will be described in the next chapter.

A good example of the different paths available with various acidic reagents is the reactions of α-terpineol (CIV) *[333]*. The most stable dehydration product of this, (CV), is formed by distillation with oxalic acid, but not by aqueous mineral acids which form mainly (CVI). Potassium hydrogen sulphate gives *anti-*

OH				
(CIV)	(CV)	(CVI)	(CVII)	(CVIII)

Saytzeff orientation (CVII), but presumably the intermediate formation of (CVI) occurs, for the product is racemic. With phthalic anhydride an optically active product (CVIII) is formed, perhaps by *cis* or *trans* bimolecular Hofmann-type elimination from the intermediate ester. Careful analyses of kinetically-controlled products have recently been carried out using gas-chromatography *[473]*.

---

* The intermediate ion is here merely formally represented; its nature is rather obscure *[25]*.

(c) Elimination from cyclic alcohols

Early work on the dehydration of the *cis*- and *trans*-isomers of (CIX) with P_2O_5 and H_3PO_4, under conditions where product isomerisation did not occur, indicated that the olefin resulting from *trans*-elimination was formed preferentially *[38, 334]*, and

(CIX)   (CX)   (CXI)   (CXII)

this was interpreted as either due to an E2 process involving $\overset{+}{R}OH_2$ or to an E1 mechanism involving a bridged ion, *cf.* (CXII). Recent ^{14}C-tracer studies have shown *[335]* that an E1 process is likely in which *trans*-elimination is probably controlled by the necessity to achieve an axial ionising conformation, but as much phenyl or hydrogen shift occurred either synchronously with or after ionisation, any deduction of mechanism from the simple product analysis is not valid. Concerted *cis*-elimination from a phosphate ester is unlikely since the corresponding xanthates give quite different products from those obtained with the above reagents, and these latter esters undoubtedly do utilise a *cis*-mechanism.

An isomeric pair in which such rearrangements do not occur is (CX), (CXI) which largely exist in the conformations shown owing to the presence of the *tert.*-butyl substituent, and which on decomposition with phosphoric or toluenesulphonic acid give Saytzeff elimination in each instance to form mainly 1-*tert.*-butylcyclohexene: this orientation being more extreme for (CX) *[336]*. These results cannot be accommodated by an E2 decomposition of an oxonium ion, but ester formation and subsequent *cis*-elimination could have occurred at the high temperatures used: it would be instructive to examine the decompositions of these possible intermediates. The likeliest possibility is a carbonium-ion mechanism, but the ions from each isomer cannot be identical, as they would be if long-lived, for they decompose to give different proportions of the isomeric olefins. An explanation similar to that put forward to accommodate similar phenomena in the menthyl series (Chap. 5, sect. 3), and which is based on a preferred axial conformation of the leaving group in an ionisation step, seems applicable; although other suggestions have been made *[337]* which stress the capabilities of forming a bridged non-classical ion (CXII) towards C_1 from the *cis*-alcohol (CX), but not from the *trans*-isomer (CXI): even when the conformation of the latter is inverted. This non-classical viewpoint would, however, seem not to predict the observed Saytzeff-like elimination of the *trans*-alcohol; for if the necessity for the protonated hydroxyl group to become axial in order to split-off is maintained (and studies of the deamination of amines, see sect. 6, have made this assumption seem very reasonable), then a bridged intermediate or transition state could readily be formed by invoking a hydrogen of the adjacent methylene group, and so Hofmann-type orientation would be expected.

A complication in all these studies is that the reaction of the ions with water either from the solvent or that formed during reaction, although not interfering with the total olefin yield (for such solvolyses merely regenerate the substrate), may well have stereochemical consequences, since the configuration of the reactant would be inverted (*cf.* sect. 6).

Qualitative data in other systems can also be similarly interpreted. Thus menthol (*i*-Pr and OH both equatorial) forms esters on treatment with HCOOH, PCl_5, and $SOCl_2$, but with 2% sulphuric acid it decomposes with Saytzeff-orientation to menth-3-ene by what must be an E1 process. Neomenthol (*i*-Pr equatorial, OH axial), which has an axial hydrogen at C_4 in its ionising conformation, reacts with all these reagents to give mainly the 3-olefin in a process which may involve an ester as an unstable intermediate *[338]*.

In *trans*-fused rings, where the limited flexibility of the *tert*-butyl-cyclohexyl system is absent and when *exo*- or *endo*-cyclic olefin formation is possible, it is found that an equatorial alcohol when dehydrated by the usual reagents generally gives predominantly (but not exclusively) the *exo*-olefin; but an axial isomer gives the *endo*-olefin *[339, 340]*. This requirement for *trans*-elimination is consistent with an E2 decomposition of an oxonium ion or an ester, but is not unambiguous evidence for this because a carbonium-ion process involving an axial conformation for ionisation and elimination will also lead to such an orientation of elimination, as explained previously for menthyl compounds (*cf*. Chap. 5, sect. 3). However, recent studies indicate that sometimes when a carbonium-ion process occurs this generalisation may break down and Saytzeff elimination may occur for both isomers to give the more stable *endo*-product *[341]*. Such an example is the reaction (104), of a sterol with (A): $HClO_4$ in AcOH* and (B): the mild but highly effective dehydrating-agent of $POCl_3$ in pyridine at $0°$ (the pyridine could act as a base in E2 or absorb the $\overset{+}{H}$ formed in E1).

The axial alcohol forms the Saytzeff product by both methods, and with method A the equatorial isomer also gave this olefin; presumably via the formation of a symmetrically solvated ion, for if an E2 decomposition of $R\overset{+}{O}H_2$ were involved the *exo*-olefin would have been expected, both in view of the necessity for achieving a *trans*-orientation for reaction and also of obeying the Hofmann rule. Method B, however, gives strict *trans*-elimination in both isomers, and the equatorial compound has to break the Saytzeff rule in order to do this. The decomposing species must

---

* Thermal *cis*-elimination from the acetate ester (if this is formed) is unlikely under these decomposition conditions.

now be the ester ROPOCl$_2$ and a normal E2-type reaction must occur, for a unimolecular thermal decomposition would lead to *cis*-elimination (*cf.* Chapter 7) and ionisation would cause mainly non-stereospecific elimination (the details of which would depend on the encumbrances of the ions and other factors). On the basis of this work it seems reasonable to expect that all compounds which obey the generalisation at the head of this paragraph will decompose by E2 mechanisms involving either oxonium ions or esters. Such bimolecular reactions would be favoured by the basic solvent in the POCl$_3$ method.

Although the mechanism is obscure, the POCl$_3$ method has been often used in structural studies in view of its believed *trans*-stereospecificity, and when the E2-geometry can be achieved the Saytzeff rule is firmly obeyed in straight chain and cyclic structures *[340–342]*. The *endo*-olefin is formed from both isomers of 4-*tert.*-butyl-1-methylcyclohexanol, eqn. (105) *[254]*; and although the

(105)

tert.-butyl group is not as efficient a conformation-holding substituent as was once believed, the direction of elimination from the *trans*-isomer (*t*-Bu,OH both equatorial) is unexpected. It is likely that an E1 mechanism occurs here, for the balance between E1 and E2 can be very delicately poised in tertiary structures. Recently, rearrangements have been detected when this reagent is used *[343]*, and this suggests an E1 process; but such mechanisms probably occur only in atypical structures and most of the structural deductions that have been based on this reaction must be valid.

The preparative use of dehydrations of the kind here described is limited nowadays, for more powerful methods, which will be discussed in the next chapter, have been developed in which difficulties due to isomerism, rearrangement, and multiplicity of products have been largely overcome. Nevertheless, the field of natural products—especially of terpenes and steroids—is full of classical dehydrations which usually yield the thermodynamically-controlled products (Saytzeff rule) and the mechanism of which can usually be reasonably interpreted on the ideas here discussed. There are some exceptions, however, for which steric or other effects have to be postulated, and there remains such intriguing problems as why the inositols (hexahydroxycyclohexanes), all save one isomer of which possess at least one *trans*-pair of OH and H substituents, should be so stable to acids, heat, and indeed to most reagents *[344]*.

An interesting class of acid-catalysed eliminations is that of hydramine fission, a typical example of which is shown in eqn.

$$
\underset{|}{\text{PhCHCHMeNHMe}} \xrightarrow{\overset{+}{H}} \underset{|}{\text{PhCHCMeNH}_2\text{Me}} \longrightarrow
$$

$$
\begin{array}{ccc}
\text{PhCHCHMeNHMe} & & \text{PhCHCMeNH}_2\text{Me} \\
| & & | \\
\text{OH} & & \text{OH}
\end{array}
\qquad (106)
$$

$$
\left[\begin{array}{c} \text{PhC}=\text{CHMe} \\ | \\ \text{OH} \end{array} \right] \longrightarrow \underset{\overset{\|}{O}}{\text{PhCCH}_2\text{Me}}
$$

(106), and which is well known in the ephredine and quinine series *[345]*. The mechanism could well be E1cB, for powerful electron-attracting groups on the β-carbons are necessary for the reaction to proceed, but nothing quantitative is known.

5. Elimination over Solid Catalysts

Only a brief mention will be made of these processes, for the detailed mechanisms (so far as they are understood) can only be appreciated by a study of surface chemistry and heterogeneous catalysis. Recent reviews summarise the vast amount of data concerning the dehydrogenations of paraffins, the dehydrations of alcohols, and the decomposition of ethers, halides etc. to olefins which occur when the vapours of these substances are passed over metals, metallic oxides or salts at 300–600° *[346, 347]*.

The dehydrations over alumina are the best studied of these reactions, and above 300° removal of water is favoured over aldehyde or ether formation, but the optimum temperature for elimination may be lower with thoria or other catalysts. Alumina usually gives better yields than more exotic combinations of catalysts and promoters when non-stereospecific elimination is required; but the rarer catalysts may be advantageous if reaction into a particular branch is wanted.

It is generally considered that dehydration is a polar rather than a radical process, but there is little agreement about the mechanism or even on the products from a particular alcohol; for a catalyst, according to its method of preparation, possesses differing abilities for causing isomerisation of the initially-formed products by double-bond or even by skeletal shifts *[348–350]*. Even at high temperatures, alumina contains a proportion of O–H bonds formed by co-ordination of water to the metal-ions of the lattice, and an initial formation of ester eqn. (107) has been suggested. An alternative

$$\overset{++}{Al}(OH) + RCH_2CH_2OH \rightarrow \overset{++}{Al}(OCH_2CH_2R) \rightarrow \overset{++}{Al}(OH) + RCH{=}CH_2 \quad (107)$$

model stresses the co-ordinative capabilities of the lone-pair of the hydroxyl-oxygen to the vacant orbital of the metal ion, *cf.* eqn. (108) *[348, 351]*, and this concept can be extended to the decom-

position of ethers. A recent careful study *[350]*, in which particular attention was paid to the prevention of isomerisation of the products, has re-affirmed earlier suggestions that the mechanism is generally carbonium ion-like, in which the acidic surface donates a proton to the alcohol which then forms an ion held on the surface. Proton loss from this ion to another part of the (microscopically) convoluted surface is not easy, and so maximum assistance from neighbouring groups is evoked and this is supposed to cause π-complex formation which can lead in extreme cases to alkyl and hydrogen shifts and so result in rearranged olefins. Intermediate π-complex character is believed to account for the very high *cis-trans* ratios of up to 4.3 (*cf.* the equilibrium value of 0.33) in a manner analogous to that in acid catalysed dehydration (sect. 4a). Such an isomer ratio is difficult to reconcile with the observation of Saytzeff orientation, but any evidence for an unusual intermediate cannot be indiscriminately applied to the vastly different conditions in solution, and the difference between the π-complex as postulated for the latter conditions and the intermediates for the rearrangements of carbonium ions (in solution) has already been discussed.

More work is required to delineate even the gross descriptions of these mechanisms. It seems that the absorption step is always rapid (as is indicated by the exchange of ROH and $H_2^{18}O$ over these catalysts at temperatures well below those at which elimination occurs), and that proton loss is the rate-determining step.

6. Elimination in Deamination

Although not a preparative method, the formation of olefins as by-products in reactions involving diazotisation has been extensively studied and presents special features of interest. It is generally considered [352] that aliphatic amines decompose by a carbonium-ion mechanism, eqn. (109A) in which the diazonium ion, in contrast to its aromatic counterpart, is highly unstable: but

$$RNH_2 \xrightarrow{HNO_2} RNHNO \longrightarrow R\overset{+}{N}_2 \begin{cases} \overset{+}{R} \longrightarrow \text{olefin etc.} \ (A) \\ B: \\ \text{olefin etc.} \qquad (B) \end{cases} \begin{array}{l} \text{E1-like} \\ \\ \text{E2-like} \end{array} \qquad (109)$$

recently the possibility of the direct breakdown at the $R\overset{+}{N}_2$ stage, eqn. (109 B) has been suggested [353]. Certainly the diazonium cation should be very reactive because of its great tendency to form elemental nitrogen, but there are several points of difference from typical E1 processes. Usually the decomposition products of a carbonium ion formed from RX are almost independent of X, but this is not so in deamination where, for example, the decomposition of the series of primary alkylamines from ethyl to nonyl yield an almost constant 24–30% of olefin [354], which is a far greater proportion than would be expected from the E1 reactions of the corresponding halides if these could be made to solvolyse under comparable conditions. Also, the ready hydride and alkyl group migrations [355], which often occur in deaminations to yield tertiary products from secondary amines and cause the 1,5 and 1,6 trans-annular shifts that have been discussed in Chap. 4, sect. 6, have parallels in other E1 reactions only when non-nucleophilic reagents are present [356] (e.g. AlCl$_3$ in benzene) or to a limited extent when the so called "limiting conditions of solvolysis" in a poorly-nucleophilic solvent such as acetic acid are employed [357, 358]. Such hydride shifts must occur intramolecularly, for no tracer is picked up from a labelled solvent [328]. The well-known Demjanov ring expansions and contractions are also common in the deaminations of cyclic amines [359], but only occur rarely under the above mentioned special conditions in the solvolyses of halides or tosylates, or the dehydrations of alcohols [360].

All this indicates that if a carbonium ion is formed on deamination, it must be modified in some way from the kind usually encountered, and the idea of a high-energy or "hot" carbonium ion has been introduced [361–364]. The ion $R\overset{+}{N}_2$ is supposed to break down almost as soon as it is formed in a reaction which is so rapid that neither solvent assistance nor neighbouring-group participation are required, as is the case for the ionisation of more stable substrates; and so an especially reactive species is formed, which possesses an unsolvated p-orbital at the α-carbon and has no counter-ion in the near vicinity. The unsolvated orbital can induce the rearrangement of suitably orientated β-substituents, hydrogen or alkyl, and the whole pattern of decomposition is different from that of a lower-energy, solvated ion-pair.

Streitwieser has challenged these views [353]: he considers that the difference in character from the typical E1 reactions indicates a different reaction mechanism and prefers to interpret the data in terms of the E2 decomposition of $R\overset{+}{N}_2$ with a solvent molecule; although the E1 mechanism is not completely excluded and can predominate in certain structures. As the diazonium ion decomposes by processes requiring low activation energies, decomposition paths which would be unimportant for slower reactions can be brought into prominence. This can be illustrated by a simple calculation: if 3 competing reactions have activation energies of 30, 25, and 20 kcal.mole^{-1}, well over 99% of the reaction will follow the last path: but if the activation energies are kept in the same ratio but are reduced to 3, 2.5, and 2 kcal.mole^{-1}, the reaction will be partitioned 10, 24, and 66% between these paths. An E2 mechanism was considered to accommodate the reactions of the stereoisomers of alicyclic systems, and also the observations of rearrangements similar to those occurring in E1 reactions when allylic amines were deaminated [365], in a more satisfactory manner than the "hot-ion" theory. We shall see later that the former phenomena can easily be accommodated on the original theory, and more recent data for substituted allylamines have indicated a large proportion of un-rearranged products which were believed to arise because the spatial distribution of the unsolvated p-orbital on the α-carbon of the hot-ion could not overlap with the rest of the system [366, 367].

The wide occurrence of Saytzeff elimination in straight-chain and cyclic systems also favours the carbonium-ion theory, for the species $R\overset{+}{N}_2$ would be expected to favour Hofmann orientation; especially if the transition state of decomposition was similar to the initial state, as it must be for such a low-activated process.

Although it is convenient to classify these reactions as E1 or E2*, the details of such fast solvolyses involving unstable intermediates

---

* The usual kinetic, isotopic, and stereochemical criteria for molecularity are inapplicable to these very fast solvolytic processes.

$R\overset{+}{N_2}$ or $\overset{+}{R}$ must be very similar, and differences are probably matters of semantics. Certainly there can be little difference between the energy profiles of the reactions, except that a shallow minimum which characterises the carbonium ion will occur in one and not the other, and if this potential-energy well is <0.5 kg cal.mole^{-1}, its presence is immaterial, for it would be by-passed by thermal vibrations. If intermediate mechanisms have any reality, or indeed any meaning, they would surely occur here. Nevertheless, certain stereochemical results can best be interpreted in terms of a duality of mechanisms, and so such a distinction can be maintained on a pragmatical basis.

The relative proportions of products from deaminations are subject to "ground-state control" [361, 368]. The intermediate carbonium or diazonium ion (if the E1-E2 distinction is maintained) is so unstable that it decomposes in the conformation from which it was produced, before rotation about a C–C bond (which requires an activation energy, 3–4 kcal.mole^{-1}, probably greater than that of deamination) can occur; and so the products are determined by the relative populations of the conformations of the original amine. For example, sec-butylamine exists in staggered conformations, by which methyl-methyl and methyl-amino group interactions are minimised, the order of population of which is (CXIII) > (CXIV) > (CXV). The 1-olefin can be readily formed from all 3, and

(CXIII)   (CXIV)   (CXV)

Deamination yields 1-butene, 25%; cis-2-butene, 19% trans-2-butene, 56%

although this is not the major product, about twice as much is formed as from the solvolysis of the corresponding halides or tosylate [368]. The ratio of trans- to cis-2-butenes is 2.9, as compared with a value of 1.1 for the solvolysis of *sec*-butyl tosylate whose carbonium ion can unrestrictedly rotate into an eliminating conformation which presents little steric hindrance to *cis*-olefin formation (see Chap. 1, sect. 1c). The higher value in deamination results from the difference in populations of the conformations (CXIII) and (CXV) which lead to the *trans*- and *cis*-olefins directly. Rearrangement of methyl from the β-carbon does not occur from the conformation (CXIV), for this would involve the formation of a relatively unstable primary carbonium ion from a secondary one, but hydride shift could occur from the other conformations and would lead to a (unsolvated?) new ion which would however break down to give formally unrearranged products. Such a re-arrangement could only be detected by ^{14}C or optical studies, and such studies of the deamination of optically-active β-amino alcohols, *e.g.* (CXVI), were best interpreted [201] on the assumption that the pinacol-like rearrangement, and also presumably elimination,

$$\underset{\text{(CXVI)}}{\overset{\displaystyle CH_3\diagdown \quad * \quad * \diagup Ph}{\underset{\displaystyle Ph^{\diagup} \mid \quad \mid \diagdown H}{\overset{\displaystyle \diagup C \!\!-\!\! C \diagdown}{\underset{\displaystyle OH \;\; NH_2}{}}}}$$

occurred through an open carbonium ion and that simultaneous β-migration and α-loss of nitrogen did not occur. Rearrangements are difficult to fit into the E2 scheme, for such exothermic reactions would possess transition states very similar to the reactant, and it is hard to see how sufficient unsaturation could be developed at the α-carbon atom to pull over the β-linked group.

If one accepts the idea of two separate mechanisms, the E1 model of a hot-ion process seems more suitable, but such a decision is uncertain for such fast processes, and is probably unnecessary.

The unique features of these reactions have usually been observed with primary and secondary amines in poorly solvating media (*e.g.* AcOH). Compounds which form more stable ions (*e.g.*, t-BuNH$_2$, t-AmNH$_2$), show the normal E1-type reactions in aqueous solution and give olefin yields and isomer proportions which are in line with those obtained from halides, tosylates, and 'onium compounds *[369]*. Presumably solvation forms a normal ion here before decomposition can set in.

The equatorial isomers of *trans*-fused cyclic amines, in which the orientation of substituents is fixed, deaminate to give predominantly the alcohol of retained configuration, and no olefin is formed. The axial epimers give an inverted alcohol and 20–50% of olefin—this olefin yield being not unduly greater than is obtained in other E1 reactions in the aqueous media usually employed *[370, 371]*. This behaviour occurs for conformationally-fixed cyclohexylamines *[370]*, 1- and 2-*trans*-decylamines *[372]*, and heterocyclics *[373]*. Substances with a flexible skeleton such as cyclopentyl and cyclohexylamines, menthylamines, carvomenthylamines, and 1- and 2-*cis*-decylamines *[370–372, 374, 375]*, in which the amino substituent is usually predominantly equatorial, mainly give retained alcohols but up to 30% elimination can occur and the yield of olefin correlates with the degree of axial character of the amino group, as estimated by conformational analysis.

Before the mechanistic speculations for the acyclic series were proposed, the above observations had been interpreted *[372]* on the basis of E1 or E2 processes; but as rearrangement or enhanced olefin yields were not very common, the former mechanism was considered to involve solvated (although still very reactive ions) rather than a hot species. Originally it was believed that an E2 decomposition of an $\overset{+}{R}\overset{}{N}_2$ ion in an axial conformation (CXVIII) would compete on nearly equal terms with the inverting substitution, but that a *trans*-E2 mechanism would not be achieved from an equatorial position and only substitution with retention, involving a pyrimidal transition state (CXVIII), would occur as

(CXVII)   (CXVIII)   (CXIX)

back-side attack to give inversion was hindered by the rest of the buckled ring system [370]. The objection to this theory was the necessity for a mechanism for equatorial isomers which contravened the known laws of substitution; but this difficulty can be circumvented by the carbonium ion hypothesis. The carbonium ion from the equatorial epimer is supposed to be solvated as it is formed, but only from the front side, for there is much steric hindrance to back-side solvation. The configuration (schematically shown in (CXIX) is only transiently held, but is maintained long enough for rapid collapse to the equatorial alcohol to occur. The carbonium ions from axial amines can be solvated from the reverse side during the actual ionisation process, for steric hindrance is now much less and so, as the ion is unstable, an inversion of configuration occurs on substitution together with elimination, for a *trans*-E2 configuration is also available.

Stable carbonium ions could become symmetrically solvated and hence cause racemisation together with the possibility of elimination from both epimers. Such solvation may occur for the carbonium ions formed in dehydrations (sect. 4), but for deaminations the ion is usually too unstable to achieve this and no unambiguous examples of this behaviour are known. Deamination of the optically-active amine (CXX) gave a 94% yield of the alcohol of the same configuration, and the lack of formation of the solvated ion and hence of racemisation was held to indicate that a synchronous

(CXX)   (CXXI)

rather than a carbonium ion process here occurred [376]. But the rate of rotation about C–C bonds is believed to be considerably slower than the rate of decomposition of a carbonium ion [201], and it seems likely that in this example the rate of solvolysis of the ion would be faster than the inversion of configuration.

As expected, E1-type rearrangements occur in labile systems and both bornyl and isobornylamine give mainly camphene (via a synartetically-assisted ionisation in the latter instance) but the former also gives some α-terpineol by ring opening *[377]*: this difference can be explained by the schemes (110). Similar ring

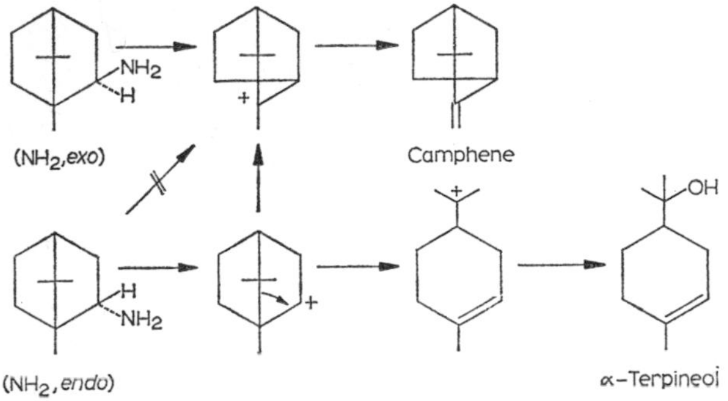

(110)*

opening occurs with fenchylamines *[378]*, eqn. (111) but not with norbornylamine *[379, 380]*, eqn. (112), for now formation of a tertiary ion from a secondary is not possible. Deamination to form

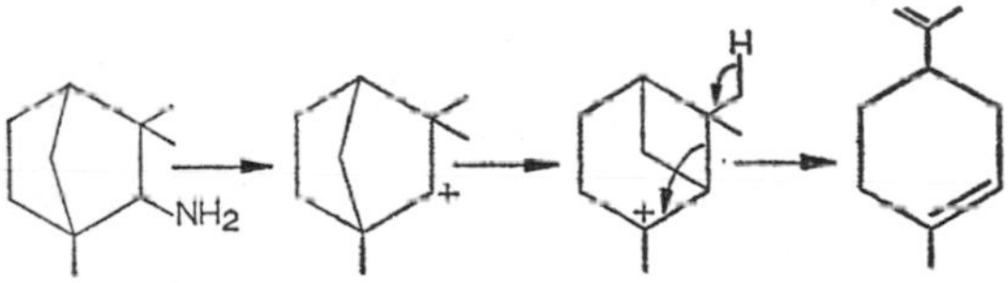

(111)

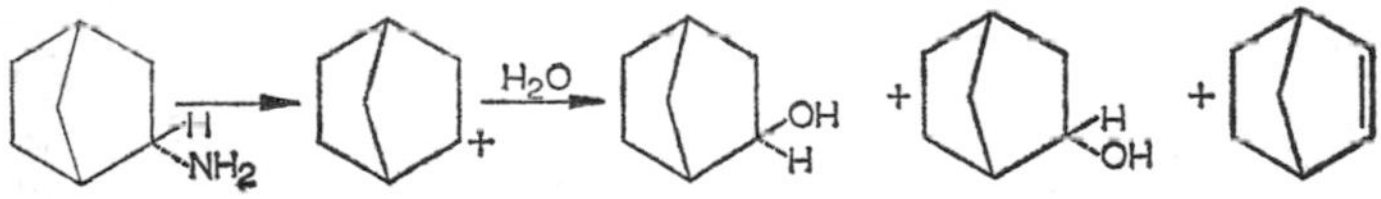

(112)*

alcohols also occur in bridgehead compounds, *e.g.* apocamphylamine (CXXI), for which uni- or bi-molecular reactions are impossible with most reagents and conditions (*cf.* p. 131) *[381]*.

trans-Fused steroids appear to provide an exception to the general

---

* See footnote on p. 151 concerning the representation of the carbonium-ion intermediates.

rule; for axial amines give olefins together with alcohols of a retained configuration [382]. In addition, for suitably substituted compounds it is found that a super-Saytzeff rule applies (cf. eqn. (113)) with the exclusive formation of one olefin: although this

conclusion is based on product isolation and more refined analysis might well pick up some minor products. These deaminations were carried out in aqueous acetic acid with little added mineral acid and the diazo-hydroxides or acetates, rather than diazonium ions, may have been the decomposing species [383]. These could undergo substitution with retention by utilising a cyclic transition state (CXXII), such as has been previously suggested for apo-

(CXXII)

camphylamine [384], and would also be expected to show Saytzeff-type orientation under E2 conditions, although the super-orientation cannot easily be explained unless one olefin is much more stable than the other. Diazo-hydroxides may well have existed in other deaminations in weakly acidic media, but are unlikely to appear at lower than about pH 2. They would possess a degree of instability similar to that of diazonium ions.

Chapter 7

PYROLYTIC ELIMINATIONS

Certain classes of compounds will decompose to form olefins at elevated temperatures in the absence of added reagent, either in the gas-phase or in inert solvents, by means of mechanisms totally different from any previously discussed. Such reactions of carboxylic esters, xanthates (the Chugaev reaction), alkyl halides, and amine-oxides (the Cope reaction)* were discovered in the last century, but during the last 15 years have been developed into elegant methods of synthesis that are preferred to the usual dehydrations and dehydrohalogenations because of the ease of technique, the excellence of the yield, and the purity of the product.

1. General Types

Examples of the 4 important classes just mentioned are given below for substrates from which only one olefin can be formed. The temperatures shown are typical for each type of compound, and

$$(CH_3)_3CCH(OCOCH_3) \xrightarrow{\text{CH}_3\;|\;500°} (CH_3)_3CCH:CH_2 + CH_3COOH \quad (114)$$

$$CH_3CH_2CH_2Br \xrightarrow{400°} CH_3CH:CH_2 + HBr \quad (115)$$

$$(CH_3)_3CCH(OCSSCH_3) \xrightarrow{180-200°} (CH_3)_3CCH:CH_2 + COS + CH_3SH \quad (116)$$
$$|$$
$$CH_3$$

$$C_6H_5CH_2CH_2\overset{+}{N}(CH_3)_2\overset{-}{O} \xrightarrow{85-120°} C_6H_5CH:CH_2 + (CH_3)_2NOH \quad (117)$$

---

* Although this reaction was discovered at the turn of the century, its potentialities were only developed by Cope and his co-workers during the last decade [242].

the olefin yield is often quantitative. The actual reaction conditions are very different. The first two classes decompose in the gas-phase, and the usual technique for esters is to sweep the vapour in a rapid stream of nitrogen over glass-wool or beads which are heated to the required temperature; thus ensuring a low contact-time. Some esters of high molecular weight (*e.g.* stearates of menthols) will however decompose at or below their boiling-points (*ca.* 300°) in the liquid state. Xanthates often decompose, partly in the gas and partly in the liquid phases, on attempted distillation; and amine-oxides are usually not isolated, but are generated *in situ* and decomposition is achieved on concentration of the solution. Discussions of the techniques, limitations, and mechanisms of these reactions are included in recent reviews [242, 385].

These pyrolyses are important synthetic methods, for back addition to and isomerisation of the initially formed olefins do not occur under the feebly acidic conditions of reaction in all cases except the halide decompositions. These last reactions, although of great theoretical importance, have been little used for preparative purposes and in some cases complications would arise. Thus for tertiary halides, although the equilibrium is well in favour of the olefin at 300–400° it is at the other extreme at the lower temperatures necessary for the working up process, unless the reaction has been carried out in the presence of a base such as ammonia which freezes the high temperature equilibrium. With iodides a side reaction between HI and the substrate to form an alkane also occurs [386].

Several mechanisms are possible for these reactions, but the best studied and the most significant theoretically involves a cyclic transition state in which a β-hydrogen is removed intramolecularly by a basic atom which is either directly α-linked or is part of an α-linked leaving group; and this mechanism is designated E_i (i = intramolecular or internal). Cyclic transition states are known which involve 4, 5 or 6 atoms, and the last type is especially favoured owing to the formation of an almost strainless ring. It is important to note that although such E_i mechanisms have been put on a firm foundation for certain reactions, they have not been proved for the bulk of the preparative processes that have been used, and alternative mechanisms (which will be discussed shortly) sometimes almost certainly intrude.

Some 4,5, and 6-membered E_i transition states are shown in (CXXIII). The directions of electron-transfer shown are purely

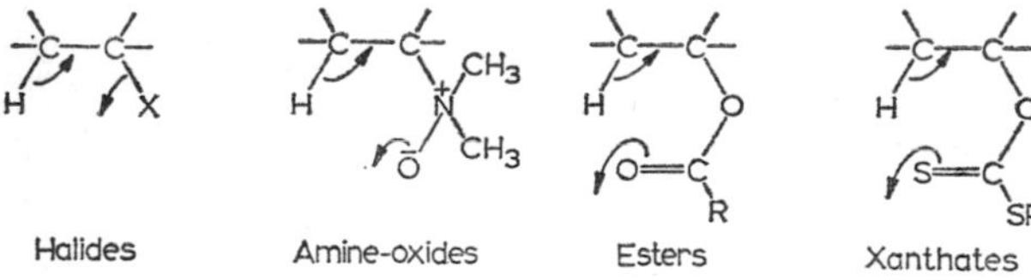

| Halides | Amine-oxides | Esters | Xanthates |

(CXXIII)

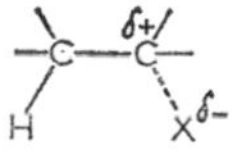

(CXXIV)

formal and take account of the usual electronegativity of the atoms, for there can be no certainty that the electrons move in any particular direction around such a system—or indeed that they move in pairs at all—for in concerted cyclic processes a distinction between heterolytic and homolytic reactions becomes untenable [387]. Only when one bond is predominantly broken in a transition state such as (CXXIV), and considerable charge separation occurs, can a meaningful designation as a heterolytic process and a comparison with such processes in solution be made, or specific experiments be designed to determine the direction of electron-transport [388].

In this chapter, the discussion will centre on the four important types of reaction mentioned above. Other pyrolyses which form olefins and probably proceed by similar mechanisms have been studied, but they are not used for synthetic purposes because of the inaccessibility of the substrates, the side reactions and/or rearrangements of products which often occur under strongly acid conditions, and the poor yields. Such reactions are the decompositions of alkyl phosphates [389], -sulphates [390], -carbonates [391], -sulphonates [392], -chloroformates [393], -chlorosulphites [394], -sulphites [395], -phosphites [396], -sulphoxides [397], -sulphones [398], -nitro-compounds [399], -borates [400], N-alkyl-amides [401], N-alkylphosphoramidates [402], aminephosphates [403], acetylated and benzoylated amines [404], β-keto acids [405], anhydrides [406], vinyl ethers [407], alcohols [408], and amines [409].

2. Fundamental Mechanisms

Quantitative kinetic studies relate almost exclusively to the gas-phase decompositions of alkyl halides and carboxylic esters. Some 25 years ago, the pioneering investigations of Daniels, Hurd, Kiastiakowsky, and others had indicated the likely mechanisms of these reactions, and over the last decade this work has been put on a sounder footing and greatly extended.

Heterogeneous processes occur easily under these reaction conditions but show irreproducible kinetics which are impossible to interpret meaningfully in terms of structure, and so recent studies have been restricted to those reactions believed to be homogeneous which occur at higher temperatures. These reactions can be isolated by means of special techniques, such as the rigid exclusion of oxygen and the use of vessels with seasoned walls which suppress surface reactions [410]. Even with seasoned vessels, however, heterogeneous decomposition may predominate at low temperatures.

Three mechanisms are found under homogeneous conditions: (i) An E_i synchronous unimolecular splitting-out of HX: or an initial homolytic fission of the C–X bond followed by, (ii) a radical non-chain process or (iii) a radical chain-reaction.

The radical non-chain scheme is shown in eqn. (118).

$$R_2CHCH_2X \xrightarrow{\text{slow}} R_2CH\overset{\bullet}{C}H_2 + \overset{\bullet}{X}$$

$$\overset{\bullet}{X} + R_2CHCH_2X \longrightarrow HX + R_2\overset{\bullet}{C}CH_2X \qquad (118)$$

$$R_2\overset{\bullet}{C}CH_2X + R_2CH\overset{\bullet}{C}H_2 \longrightarrow R_2C:CH_2 + R_2CHCH_2X$$

A radical-chain reaction involves the first two steps, but the radical thus formed reacts in a chain-propagation step, eqn. (119). The smaller bond energy of C–X than C–H causes this reaction to occur rather than the last step of eqn. (118), except under special circum-

$$R_2\dot{C}CH_2X \longrightarrow R_2C{:}CH_2 + \dot{X} \tag{119}$$

stances. These schemes are not all-embracing and variations can occur: for instance, β-hydrogen abstraction will lead to a radical capable of ejecting X—a so called "propagating-radical"—but if an α- or γ-hydrogen is removed, a "stopping-radical" will be obtained which cannot decompose to yield olefin, but which nevertheless can react with a substrate molecule to generate a propagating radical. A full analysis of such possibilities has been given [411]. The E_i, the non-chain, and usually the chain mechanisms obey first-order kinetics and additional criteria must be employed to differentiate between them. E_i processes are unaffected by radical inhibitors (nitric oxide, propylene, and especially cyclohexene) and show no induction period, whereas both forms of radical process exhibit the converse behaviour and are much affected by the presence of oxygen and halogens, and in particular can be suppressed (to varying extents) by inhibitors. A special requirement for a radical non-chain reaction is that the observed activation energy must be equivalent to the bond energy of C_α–X, because the rate of the overall process is the same as that of the initial step: if the activation energy is less than this value, then such a process is excluded. No similar requirement is necessary for the chain mechanism, because analysis shows that the observed rate constant is now a function of the rate constants of the individual steps, and the observed activation energy is usually relatively low (which accounts for the ready incidence of these reactions), and less than that of the initial homolytic fission.

A criterion for E_i, often considered the best, is the observation of a critical low-pressure region where the Maxwell-Boltzmann distribution of energy is not maintained, and an intrusion into which results in a decrease in the calculated first-order rate constant and a change to second-order kinetics (the Hinshelwood-Lindemann fall-off). Such a phenomenon has been observed for several alkyl chlorides, and the quantitative behaviour has been reasonably interpreted on the basis of the various theories of unimolecular gas-reactions developed by Hinshelwood, Kassel, Slater and others [412].

Most of the simpler alkyl chlorides and bromides have been carefully studied and the mechanisms dissected [413, 414]. Poly-halides usually exhibit chain processes; primary halides show mixed chain and E_i mechanisms, the proportion of the latter increasing with homology; and secondary (straight chain and cyclic) and tertiary halides mainly decompose by E_i mechanisms. Chain reactions require the presence of relatively weak C–H bonds and tend to appear for such compounds as β-phenylethyl bromide and iso- and sec-butyl bromides [415]. The differing tendencies for chain or non-chain reactions in different series can be attributed in certain cases to the formation of an olefin which acts as a chain inhibitor, or what is more likely, to varying tendencies for the formation of chain-propagating and -stopping radicals. Radical non-chain examples are rare, for they require the formation of relatively stable alkyl radicals: one such case occurs for allyl bromide [416].

An elucidation of the different rate constants for the chain steps is difficult and would not add greatly to an understanding of the effect of structure on rate and mechanism. Consequently, the most fruitful field of exploration has been of pure E_i processes in which radical components are suppressed by inhibitors, and such a state of affairs has been achieved for most of the lower alkyl mono-chlorides and bromides [413, 414]. The decomposition of the corresponding iodides is bedevilled by the intrusion of heterogeneous reactions and radical processes (because of the low C–I bond energy); but nevertheless the E_i pathway has probably been isolated for iso-propyl, and iso- and sec-butyl compounds [386, 417]. Certain esters [418], ethers [407], alcohols [408], and amines [409] have also been shown to utilise this mechanism.

On the basis of the criteria stated above, a body of reproducible, self-consistent data for E_1 has been built-up. Suggestions [419] that such reactions involve chain processes which are initiated and terminated on the walls of the containing vessel (as in gas-phase oxidations) but which propagate and react in the gas-phase, seem groundless; for although these would have a rate not very dependent on the ratio of surface area to volume, they would be inhibited by the usual additives, or by the seasoning of the walls. Outside the alkyl halide series, however, the degree of incursion of heterogeneous or chain processes is uncertain. Most studies of esters have been perfunctory, and the preparative techniques (using glass-wool and beads) may well involve surface catalysed or radical reactions. Xanthate and amine-oxide pyrolyses have been seldom studied from this viewpoint, and although the interpretation of their stereochemistry (*cf.* sect. 3) is in accord with the E_1 mechanism, nevertheless it is disturbing to find that xanthates, as they are usually prepared, contain peroxides. These impurities can be removed by distillation under reduced pressure or by washing with ferrous solutions to give "stable" forms of xanthates, which decompose at a considerably higher temperature than do the untreated "unstable" forms, but which apparently give identical products [420].

In the following discussion only E_1 processes will be considered but it must be appreciated that many of the references to xanthates, esters, and amine-oxides could involve mixed mechanisms.

3. Stereochemistry

It was realised in the early studies that unimolecular E_1 reactions would probably utilise the cyclic transition states previously described, perhaps involving initial transient hydrogen-bonding between the β-hydrogen atom and the leaving group, and that this would lead to stereospecific *cis*-elimination [421]. As previously explained, such a stereochemistry is opposed by quantal forces in the more common solution processes, which however proceed under much less forcing conditions. Originally it was thought that xanthates extracted the β-hydrogen by attack of the sulphur of the thio-ether linkage (CXXV)*, but recently the alternative (CXXVI) has been proved by an ingenious juxtaposition of ^{13}C and ^{34}S kinetic isotope effects [422].

(CXXV)   (CXXVI)

(a) Acyclic systems

The deduction of the stereo-course of acyclic decompositions is possible in a few cases where geometrical isomers are formed. Almost exclusive *cis*-elimination in Chugaev and Cope pyrolyses has been demonstrated in the familiar (cf. Chap. 1, sect. 2a) 3-phenyl-2-butyl [423], and 1,2-diphenylpropyl systems [424]. The only illustration for esters is that the reaction of the enantiomers of PhCHDCHPhOCOCH$_3$ both gave *trans*-stilbenes, but that one olefin contained all the initial complement of deuterium, whereas the other contained none [49]. This could only be accounted for by a *cis*-elimination; the great preference for *trans*-olefin formation being caused by the necessity to avoid the eclipsing of the phenyl groups in the transition states (CXXVII) and (CXXVIII). It

(CXXVII)   (CXXVIII)   (CXXIX)

* By this mechanism the three reaction products (olefin, COS, RSH) could be formed in one concerted step and the large exothermicity of the overall reaction utilised as a driving force.

should be noted that *cis*-elimination does not necessarily demand an exact eclipsing of bonds as shown, but that a staggered conformation (CXXIX) could be utilised. The latter stereochemistry would be favoured for 6-membered transition states for here the geometry permits ample bridging space to the syn-clinal positions: 5-, and certainly 4-membered rings might be forced to use a more totally eclipsed conformation.

(b) Cyclohexyl systems: esters and xanthates

Much greater detail is available concerning the stereochemistry of the decomposition of alicyclic substrates. Barton was the first to appreciate the general necessity and significance of *cis*-elimination in E_i processes in complex structures, and he showed that this concept correctly interpreted the directions of elimination of the esters and xanthates of many cyclic natural products: furthermore, he used these reactions as tools for predicting some then unknown configurations of such compounds [425]. Evidence for *cis*-elimination can be obtained by adoption of the argument used to predict the direction of elimination in menthyl systems as in Chap. 5, sect. 3, and it is found that such predictions are in accord with experiment [27]. Studies of rigidly held *cis*- and *trans*-isomers such as (CXXX), also have verified the great predominance of *cis*-

cis and trans
(CXXX)

(CXXXIa)

(CXXXIb)

over *trans*-processes [426]. In no case however has *cis*-elimination been proved for halide decompositions: a point which is significant in view of the likelihood of an ion-pair mechanism in these cases (*cf*. sect. 3b and sect. 6).

More detail can be appreciated by consideration of the general conformational equilibrium (CXXXI). It is likely that staggered conformations would be utilised in cyclic systems, for perfectly eclipsed structures would require a chair to boat interconversion, but it must be also borne in mind that at the elevated temperatures of these reactions both the chair-boat and all-chair equilibria would be considerably displaced in favour of the less stable forms (this particularly applies to the former equilibrium, which has a larger energy difference between its participants than the other). When the leaving group X is equatorial (CXXXIa), it is equidistant from the two hydrogens which are gauche to it on the adjacent carbon atom, and so either of these might be expected to be available for *cis*-elimination. If X is axial (CXXXIb), the distance to a suitably orientated β-hydrogen is the same, although now only one such atom is available in a particular branch. However, it is found that an equatorial X removes an axial hydrogen, *i.e.* Hβ′ in (CXXXIa), rather than an equatorial one; although the geometrical environment would seem similar for the two reactions. An axial X is obliged to abstract an equatorial hydrogen. Although the angular distortion in all cases is similar, the tendency to form a planar cyclic transition state between two equatorial groups apparently leads to the occurrence of non-bonded interactions between the compressed axial hydrogens whereas in the alternative transition state such interaction is decreased. This stereo-requirement accounts for the formation of isopropylidenes by *cis*-cyclohexane diols under conditions when the *trans*-isomers do not react [427], and it is well illustrated by the reactions (120) of the *cis*- and *trans*-2-methylcyclohexyl acetates [428]. An a,e* elimination can occur towards either branch of the *trans*-isomer and a mixture of olefins results, but for the *cis*-acetate only an e,e transition state could lead to the 1-methylcyclohexene, and so the other 3-olefin is almost exclusively formed: the fact that some 1-olefin is produced indicates that e,e orientations are not completely forbidden. This restriction to e,e elimination shows that a tendency to planarity must be present in a 6-membered transition state, and some buckling of

---

* The abbreviations a,e and e,e will be used for *cis*-eliminations between axial and equatorial, and between two equatorial substituents respectively.

the carbon skeleton must occur. An alternative explanation could be that the *cis*-acetate existed and hence reacted almost entirely through the conformation of the right hand side of the above

(120)

equilibrium; but in view of the small difference in size of the two substituents and of the elevated temperature at which the reaction proceeded, this seems unlikely. It has been considered that the ratio of elimination rates for the conformationally "fixed" *cis*- and *trans*-isomers of 4-*tert*-butylcyclohexyl acetate reflects the difference in energy of the initial states, for the same product is formed from each isomer by means of a,e eliminations [429]. Such a deduction however assumes that the transition states for the two conformers are identical in energy and also there is some doubt if the conformations of the ester are fixed to the extent which was once believed, especially at elevated temperatures.

The restriction on elimination from e,e orientations is broken when a β-hydrogen atom which is activated by a powerful electron-withdrawing substituent is involved. *trans*-2-*p*-Toluenesulphonyl-cyclohexyl xanthate can (*cf.* projections in eqn. (120)) eliminate from a,e conformations towards either C_2 or C_6; and as might be expected [430] the elimination is entirely of the activated hydrogen on C_2. The stable conformation of the *cis*-isomer has an axial xanthate group and an equatorial sulphone group and so an a,e conformation for elimination can only be achieved towards C_6;

however, the sole reaction product is the olefin formed by loss of the activated hydrogen on C_2 and so inversion to the less stable conformation, followed by an e,e elimination must have occurred. This explanation pre-supposes a concerted process: a two-step process could also be envisaged as for the *trans*-eliminations of similar structures discussed in Chap. 4, sect. 2.

In structures for which either *endo*- or *exo*-cyclic olefin formation is possible it seems, despite some controversy, that the more stable *endo*-isomer is preferred. Thus 1-methylcyclohexyl acetate gives 75% of this isomer [431], and as there is unlikely to be considerable double-bond formation in the transition state (see later), this orientation probably depends on entropy effects,—elimination into the ring is favoured by the availability of suitably orientated hydrogens whereas reaction to give the *exo*-olefin requires a "freezing" of the ready rotation of the methyl group.

(c) Cyclohexyl systems: amine-oxides and halides

A different situation occurs for reactions which involve 4- or 5-membered transition states, for only if the C_β–H and C_α–X bonds eclipse can the necessary atoms be brought into close enough proximity to ensure reaction. A striking difference in the course of such reactions to those involving 6-membered rings occurs in the decomposition of (CXXXII), which gives the less stable *exo*-olefin

(CXXXII)

(97%) [244] as compared with the predominant formation of the *endo*-isomer (75%) from the corresponding acetate and xanthate. For the amine-oxide, a completely eclipsed transition state cannot be formed towards a ring hydrogen unless the energetically unfavourable boat-conformation is involved, and so reaction takes place largely into the methyl group where only an eclipsing of a methyl group has to be overcome at a much lower expenditure of energy.

The pyrolyses of the esters, halides, and amine-oxides of the menthyl isomers provide an interesting illustration of the stereorequirements of different substrates. Orientational data are shown in Table 16,—the conformations of these compounds are given on p. 117—and assuming (what is only well established for the chloride) that all these reactions are E_1^*, these differences can be reasonably interpreted.

TABLE 16

PYROLYSIS PRODUCTS OF MENTHYL COMPOUNDS

	2-ene (%)	3-ene (%)	Ref.
Menthyl acetate, xanthate	*ca.* 30	*ca.* 70	[27,432]
Neomenthyl xanthate	*ca.* 80	*ca.* 20	[27]
Menthyldimethylammonium oxide	64	36	[258]
Neomenthyldimethylammonium oxide	100	0	[258]
Menthyl chloride	25	75	[433]
Neomenthyl chloride	Not investigated		

Elimination from the acetates and xanthates can occur from non-eclipsed gauche neighbouring orientations, and the direction is unrestricted for both chair-conformations of menthyl compounds and Saytzeff orientation results. Neomenthyl derivatives are required to invert into the unstable conformation (*i*-Pr axial, X equatorial) in order to permit *cis*-elimination to give the 3-ene; but as even then such elimination requires the loss of 2 adjacent equatorial groups, this mode is unfavourable and cannot compete well with the stereo-unrestricted decomposition to the 2-ene (Hofmann orientation).

The amine-oxides require complete eclipsing of the α- and β-linked

---

* E_1 in this context means a non-radical reaction. It is not known if a synchronous or an intramolecular ion-pair process occurs for the halides (vida infra).

leaving groups and so a boat-conformation of the cyclohexane skeleton is necessary. When this is achieved in the menthyl case, transition states leading to either 2- or 3-menthenes are available, but steric and statistical factors (see later) cause the former olefin to predominate. The neomenthyl example cannot achieve a completely eclipsed transition state for elimination towards C_4 for only the isopropyl group can be eclipsed with the amino-oxide group, and so, in this case, no 3-menthene is formed. Menthyl chloride should possess a similar (or more stringent!) stereo-requirement to the corresponding amine-oxide, but the opposite orientation of elimination is obtained. It will be shown later that considerable C–Cl heterolysis, perhaps even amounting to ion-pair formation, must occur in this transition state and hence the expected restriction may be relaxed.

(d) Larger-ring systems

A comparison of the tendencies of Hofmann and Cope degradations to give cis- and trans-olefins from large ring amines has already been given, and the results attributed to the need to minimise non-bonded interactions for the two different type of transition state (Chap. 5, sect. 4). A similar orientation of elimination occurs for cyclo-octyl, nonyl and decyl xanthates [434, 470] and probably also for acetates, although the results in the latter case are uncertain because isomerisation and decomposition of the initially formed cyclic olefins to straight-chain products can occur at the temperature of pyrolysis [434b].

Several other systems have been investigated. The percentage of endo- and exo-cyclic olefins and the cis-trans ratios of the former have been measured for a series of amine-oxides (CXXXIII) with $n = 5$ to 10. For $n = 6$, the leaving group is equatorial and an

(CXXXIII)   (CXXXIV)   (CXXXV)

eclipsed transition state can only be easily formed with the exo-methyl group, and so a 97% yield of the *exo*-olefin is achieved. In all the other examples the leaving group is either already eclipsed with a ring hydrogen in the initial state ($n = 5$ and 7) or sufficient flexibility is present for such a condition to be attained without an excessive energy expenditure ($n = 8$, 9 and 10), and 97–99% yields of the more stable *endo*-olefin are obtained [435]. The *cis-trans* ratio (which favours the former) can be explained in a manner similar to that for Hofmann degradation.

Certain other reactions are of interest in delineating the flexibility of cyclic systems. Azacyclohexylamine-oxides (CXXXIV) and the lactones (CXXXV) are stable at 150° and 500–600° when the ring is 5- or 6-membered [436, 437], but for larger rings the basic (*exo-cyclic*) oxygen atom can be orientated to attack a neighbouring β-hydrogen and ring fission occurs at these temperatures. As most naturally-occurring nitrogen bases possess heterocyclic 6-membered rings, this restriction means that the Cope degradation has not the general utility of the Hofmann method for structural investigations.

4. Olefin Yield and Stereospecificity

Pyrolytic methods are unsurpassed among eliminations for the yield, purity and predictability of products. No rearrangement is detected even for such labile structures as Bu^tCHXCH_3 (X = acetate or xanthate), and the mild conditions of the Cope reaction are much less prone to cause rearrangement than Hofmann degradation, even in the morphine-codeine series of alkaloids [438]; and in addition the olefin yields are almost invariably larger from the former reactions. Exhaustive methylation and Hofmann degradation of amines (CXXXVI) gives up to 4% of cyclic olefins

$$(CH_2)_nCHCH_2NR_2$$

$$(CXXXVI)$$

formed by ring-expansion [244], a reaction which has its parallel in ester pyrolyses [439], but amine-oxide degradation shows none of this behaviour. Some other side reactions can occur, but these are not usually characteristic of the elimination processes. Thus under the high temperatures required for ester pyrolysis, ring-scission of a cyclic olefin or isomerisations of the substrate before decomposition have been found, but these are unimportant under the much milder Chugaev or Cope conditions. Rearrangement in Chugaev reactions can occur when no β-hydrogen is available as in the benzyl, neopentyl, and fenchyl compounds [385], and somtimes even in specially activated structures of the bornyl type in which normal *cis*-elimination is possible [440].

Although *cis*-stereospecificity of olefin formation is usually high, there are many cases where appreciable (up to 25%) products of *trans*-elimination are obtained: one such example (the decomposition of menthyl chloride) has already been noted. These can be attributed to the incursion of mechanisms other than E_i, and will be considered in sect. 6.

5. The Detailed Mechanism of E_i Reactions

The relative importance and situation of bond-making and -breaking in the transition states of these reactions can be deduced, as for solvolytic reactions, from the effect of substituents on rate. As would be expected, there is a considerable variation between, and within, the various types.

(a) Alkyl halides

Probably the most careful and extensive of all gas-kinetic studies have been devoted to these compounds and it is found that C_α–X breakage dominates the transition state [414]. The pre-exponential Arrhenius factors* of all these reactions fall in the range $10^{12.7}$ to $10^{14.5}$, with a modal value of $10^{13.5}$ (all in sec^{-1}), and thus the effect of changing structure can be discussed in terms of the change of activation energy. Some values are given in Table 17 and are compared with the energy required for the homolytic and heterolytic

---

* Gas-kinetic studies are usually reported in terms of the A-factor, rather than ΔS^*—the common usage for solution reactions.

TABLE 17

ACTIVATION ENERGIES [415] OF HALIDE ELIMINATIONS
IN THE GAS-PHASE IN THE RANGE 300–400°, AND HETEROLYTIC
AND HOMOLYTIC DISSOCIATION ENERGIES
(All energies in kcal.mole^{-1})

	$EtBr$	Pr^iBr	Bu^tBr	$EtCl$	Pr^iCl	Bu^tCl
Ea (expt.)	54	48	42	60	51	41
D (R + X)	67	68	64	81	82	78
D ($\overset{+}{R}$ + $\overline{X}$)	184	156	140	193	166	150

fission of C_α–X in the gas-phase. A dramatic effect of α-methylation is found, and at 400° the relative rates of elimination from ethyl, iso-propyl, and *tert*-butyl bromides are 1, 170 and 32,000; at lower temperatures the rate ratios are much larger[*]. On the other hand, methylation at the β-carbon atom has little effect on the rate, and the activation energies for such substituted primary, secondary, and tertiary halides are at most 1–2 kcal.mole^{-1} lower than the values quoted for the unsubstituted members of each class: thus the acidity of the β-hydrogens appears unimportant. Double-bond formation in the transition state is also small, for β-phenylethyl and β-vinylethyl halides decompose at about the same rate as the corresponding ethyl halide, and α-phenylethyl bromide compares closely with the *tert*-butyl bromide; these being exact parallels to the situations in unimolecular solvolyses.

The controlling influence of C_α–X bond lability is well shown in the α-halogenated series which exhibit the rate order (121), and a splendid example is the 10^{10}-fold increase of rate (at 200°) when

$$CH_3CX_3 > CH_3CHX_2 > XCH_2CH_2X > CH_3CH_2X \qquad (121)$$

[*] Only when the fastest reacting members of a series have the lowest activation energy can an extrapolation to lower temperatures be made with the knowledge that the relative rates will stay in the same order.

an α-hydrogen in ethyl bromide is replaced by a methoxy group [441]—again this has an exact counterpart in solvolytic reactions.

All the above behaviour is analogous to that of E1 reactions in solution, and the activation energy correlates with the dissociation energy for ionisation in the gas-phase, rather than with the energy to form radicals. In addition, the Saytzeff rule is obeyed for these pyrolyses as has been shown by analysis of the isomers obtained from α-branched halides. Maccoll was thus led to the conclusion that the gas-phase and solvolytic eliminations were comparable, and he postulated a "quasi-heterolytic" transition state (CXXXVII) for the former, involving considerable charge separation [417].

(CXXXVII) (CXXXVIII) (CXXXIX)

Such a comparison should best hold for solvolyses under limiting conditions (cf. p. 121) when all the intramolecular capabilities for the facilitation of reaction are evoked, and the solvent plays a relatively minor role.

Much other information is well correlated by this idea. The Arrhenius A-values for such reactions are those for "normal" unimolecular reactions, and imply very little restriction of freedom in the transition state*. Any large contribution of structures such as (CXXXVIII), which would best be classified as homolytic, would require severe restrictions compared with the initial state, but no restriction is required for a transition state in which the β-hydrogen bond is not appreciably broken. Another line of supporting evidence is the magnitude of β-deuterium isotope effects, which have been found to be about 2.0 for ethyl bromide and chloride [442] and isopropyl chloride [417]. Insomuch as this is nearly the maximum value predicted to correspond to a complete loss of a

---

* Cf. the cyclic Diels-Alder processes which can have A-factors as low as 10^6 sec^{-1}.

C–H stretching vibration at the temperature of these experiments, this could imply a transition state in which there was extensive proton transfer. However, a 4-centred transition state (CXXXVIII) would involve much bond bending, rather than stretching, and this would considerably reduce the size of the maximum isotope effect. A better explanation is that a secondary isotope effect on the rate of ionisation is observed (*cf.* Chap. 1, sect. 1c), and the apparent agreement with the maximum theoretical primary effect is merely fortuitous. Such secondary effects would be important under the "limiting conditions" of the gas-phase, and similar effects, which are almost temperature independent, are well known to be of about the same magnitude in unimolecular solvolysis.

The principle of microscopic reversibility provides more support for the heterolytic mechanism: the reverse reaction, the addition of HX to an olefin in the gas-phase, probably proceeds through an intermediate (CXXXIX), and so the elimination reaction would likewise be expected to involve this structure.

This heterolytic view of gas reactions has been taken to an extreme in the suggestion that an ion-pair is formed: and this must be completely undissociated, for no solvent is available to facilitate charge separation [443]. The large energy of ionisation of halides in the gas-phase (Table 17) refers to dissociation, and it has been argued that as the energy to cause ion-separation may well be 100–120 kcal.mole [1], the energy for ion-pair formation would be only 50–60 kcal.mole^{-1}—in good (and probably fortuitous) agreement with the experimental activation energy. It is not clear if an experimental (or indeed a physical) distinction can be made between a reaction involving an ion-pair and one involving a polarised bond, for the entropy and substituent effects should be similar in each case, and the techniques available in solutions such as the exchange of tracer and the racemisation of an optically-active substrate prior to elimination might not be applicable in the gas-phase. As free ions do not occur, the product distribution from RX should be dependent on X (*cf.* the situation for solvolyses) and it is not surprising that different *sec*-butyl halides give widely different ratios of butene-1 and butene-2 [444, 445]. The formation of rearranged olefins from neopentyl chloride [446] (which cannot directly give an olefin by an E_i mechanism) and certain other halides [447], is consistent with an ion-pair intermediate.

A few other types of compound have been found to undergo E_i reactions. Ethanol, *n*- and iso-propanol, and *n*-butanol decompose via homogeneous radical chains: but *tert*-butanol and *tert*-pentanol show the former type [408]. Recently, homogeneous catalysis of the gas-phase decomposition of *tert*-butanol and isopropanol by hydrogen halides has been found in which the activation energy is lowered by some 25 kcal.mole^{-1} compared with the normal reaction [448]. This is another analogy to solvolytic reactions, and an ion-pair $R\overset{+}{O}H_2\overline{X}$ is probably involved, although cyclic transition states cannot be discounted. Certain ethers also probably undergo such catalysis via a similar mechanism, but at a greater rate since the oxygen is now more basic than in alcohols.

(b) Esters

The description of the transition states is much less certain for this class, for few rigorous kinetic studies have been carried out, and the effect of structural change on rate has been mainly deduced from experiments under preparative conditions [385]. It has generally been assumed that such reactions proceeded via E_i mechanisms, but radical processes are known to occur when esters with no β-hydrogens are pyrolysed [474] and they may appear under other conditions. The use of a minimum temperature of pyrolysis and non-seasoned glass surfaces, without the rigid exclusion of oxygen, would seem ideal for the introduction of such reactions. Strictly, the structural effects on rate should only be discussed for kinetically controlled E_i decompositions, but owing to the paucity of data the other results obtained under preparative conditions will be also considered, although it is not clear what weight should be ascribed to them. The incidence of mixed mechanisms might be responsible for the several contradictory reports that have appeared concerning ester pyrolyses. Thus there have been disagreements about the isomer-ratios from various secondary esters [431], and it has been claimed [449], and disputed [431], that isomer ratios vary with the temperature of the pyrolysis. Such discordant reports may also be due to the presence of acid, which caused product-isomerisation on the cracking columns in certain cases.

A whole spectrum of transition states with different degrees of bond-breaking and -forming are available for E_i reactions; but, as for E2 reactions in solution, it is convenient to consider three special cases which appear to be important in practice, and in which particular bonds are broken. These are shown below:

(A)   (B)   (C)

E2-like "heterolytic"   Concerted "homolytic"   E1cB-like "heterolytic"

Ester pyrolyses are slightly endothermic (*ca.* 5 kcal.mole^{-1} as calculated from bond-energy data) and this suggests (*cf.* Chap. 1, sect. 3a) that the electronic configuration in this state is intermediate in character, but with a leaning towards that of the reaction product rather than the reactant. Pyrolyses of alkyl halides are slightly more endothermic than those of esters but here all the kinetic data indicate that the nuclear configuration in the transition state resembles the initial state, and so these 4-centre reactions may be cases where the position on the reaction coordinate is determined mainly by the breaking of one bond (C_α–X) and this position can be unrelated to the geometrical similarity of the rest of the activated molecule to the reactants or the products.

The only reliable approach to the structure of the transition state is through a study of substituent effects, but it must be realised that no single model can accommodate all these effects, for the introduction of an unusual group may bias the structure in a way quite atypical for simpler compounds.

Accurate kinetic data for E_i reactions of α-methylated alkyl acetates are given in Table 18 *[418]*. The trend indicates that

C–O fission plays a much less important role in the determination of the reaction rate than C_α–X breakage does for alkyl halides, and consequently these reactions have been considered to proceed by

TABLE 18

RELATIVE RATES ETC. FOR α-METHYLATED ALKYL ACETATES

	Ea	$Log_{10}A$	Rel. rate (400°)	Rel. rate (100°)
EtOAc	48	13.7	1	1
Pr^{i}OAc	45	13.0	26	10^2
Bu^{t}OAc	40	13.3	1660	10^5

an internal E2-like attack of the carbonyl oxygen on an acidic hydrogen, utilising a transition state of type A in which O–H bond formation is dominant. Rather than an analogy with ionisation processes in solution, a correspondence of substituent effects with base-catalysed E2 decompositions of sulphonium salts (which utilise an E1cB-like transition state) has been suggested [417, 418]; but although the relative rates of these gas and liquid phase reactions are closely comparable at 400° and 55° respectively, the analogy becomes rather strained when the comparison is made at 100° (cf. Tables 10 and 18) and the worth of such an approach is doubtful. These, and other results, have also been interpreted on the basis of a model B for the transition state, which is quasi-homolytic and involves little charge separation, but is highly concerted [385]. There are various limitations to both the above views and a model C seems equally capable of explaining the observed data, but at the moment not enough accurate kinetically controlled rate and isotope (such as ^{18}O) data are available for a firm decision to be possible.

The frequency factors for the α-methylated alkyl esters are normal (although for certain other esters they can be ca. 10^{11}–10^{12}), and this would be inconsistent with models A and B, but not C, for the loss of entropy in the restriction of a bulky acetate group into a cyclic transition state should be large. The esters of a particular alcohol with strong acids decompose more readily than those of weak acids [450, 451], and this has been considered to eliminate structure A. Such an interpretation neglects, however, the effects of such a change on the ease of C–O fission.

Ethyl-d_5 [452], 1,2-diphenylethyl-d_1 [49], and 1-methylcyclohexyl-d_4-acetates [453] show β-deuterium isotope effects of 2 to 3 which are close to the values expected for the complete loss of a C–H stretching vibration at the temperatures involved, and so are consistent with all 3 models of the transition state. Perhaps the considerable contribution of a bending, rather than a stretching vibration, as required by models A and B would be expected to produce a smaller effect; but certainly the secondary effect cannot be evoked here, as in alkyl halides, for now the C–O heterolysis is small.

α- and β-Phenyl, and α-methoxy substituents are reported [453, 454] to have small effects on the rate (as compared with the unsubstituted compounds) and so it has been concluded, in contradiction to the above, that β H transfer and also double-bond formation in the transition states are unimportant. These results were, however, obtained in qualitative studies under non-kinetically controlled conditions.

Evidence for the degree of involvement of the C–H bond should also be obtainable from the direction of elimination in secondary and tertiary structures, just as is done for reactions in solution. Originally it was believed that the Hofmann rule was exclusively obeyed for ester pyrolyses, but the advent of improved analytical techniques (especially gas-chromatography) has shown that considerable (but never major) proportions of the Saytzeff-type olefins are formed from simple alkyl esters [385]. An interpretation of the published data is difficult as the bulk was obtained under conditions of completely uncertain mechanism. A recent conclusion is that the obedience to the Hofmann rule is not due to inductive control, stimulated by a transition state of type A, but rather to the operation of a statistical effect whereby more primary hydrogens are available for elimination than are secondaries *[385]*. On this view a transition state of type B was adopted for all esters in which the effects of hydrogen acidity, olefin-stability, and steric interaction were all small, and often cancelled out, and for which polarisation and polarisability effects were unimportant. This statistical effect can account for the orientation in several cases: for instance *sec*-butyl and *tert*-pentyl acetates gave 60–40% and 75–25% distributions of the Hofmann and Saytzeff products respectively under both preparative *[429]* and kinetically controlled E_i conditions *[455]*, and these are exactly the olefin proportions which are to be expected from the relative availability of the β-hydrogens on each branch. However, it should be noted that random statistical distribution of products would also be expected with a radical mechanism.

Statistical control is favoured by the observation *[429]* that the proportions of olefin isomers from *tert*-pentyl acetate was the same at 350°, 400° and 500°,—*i.e.*, the activation energy was the same for the formation of each isomer—but others have found *[449, 455]* a transition to Hofmann control as the temperature was increased*. In view of the fact that (as in most preparative experiments) the half-life of the reaction was very small in the former set of experiments, it is possible that the decompositions, although nominally at different temperatures, in practice all occurred at the top of the pyrolysis tube at an undefined, almost constant, lower temperature. Another complicating factor is that the stabilities of the terminal and non-terminal olefins become comparable as the temperature is increased above about 300°, and so under pyrolysis conditions the usual effect of electromeric substituents could be partially reversed.

Statistical effects are certainly reasonable, for the energy which a molecule obtains by collision has to be reorganised into the bonds which are to be broken before reaction can proceed and the chances of this happening for C_β–H bonds are obviously dependent on the number available in a particular branch; but also polar effects

---

* It was suggested that Saytzeff orientation occurred in liquid-phase pyrolyses at low temperatures; but that at higher temperatures, in the gas-phase, the other rule was obeyed.

should be able to direct this redistribution of energy, and there is no reason to assume that only the transition state of type B can accommodate these effects.

The controlling influences of these pyrolyses are not clear and more extensive, careful kinetic studies are necessary. When polar or unsaturated substituents are introduced, the energy pathways to particular transition states are lowered just as in the corresponding cases in solution. Acetic anhydride (CXL) decomposes to ketene via an E_i mechanism 5,600 times faster than does ethyl acetate

(CXL)   (CXLI)

under the same conditions [406], and this has been interpreted in terms of a transition state with predominant O–H bond formation to the activated β-hydrogen; although the $\log_{10}A$-factor (12.1) seems remarkably high for this mechanism. Vinyl ethers (CXLI) [407] do not show such a rate enhancement and should more resemble the esters, but their A-factors are now slightly smaller ($\log_{10}A \sim 11.1$ to 11.6). Other β-substituents such as $\cdot NMe_2$, $\cdot NO_2$, and $\cdot CO_2Me$ can also influence this pathway, and lead to a breakdown of the Hofmann rule [456].

Phenyl substituents would be expected to favour extensive double-bond formation in the transition state; and certainly for para-substituted 1,3-diphenylpropyl-2-acctates the stability of the two possible olefins appears to control the direction of elimination [454]: however such factors seem unimportant for 1-phenyl-2-p-substituted phenylethyl acetates [457].

(c) Xanthates

It is dangerous to speculate by analogy with the esters about the detailed path of these reactions in view of the widely different conditions; but despite the presence of peroxides in the reacting systems, the frequent observation of nearly stereospecific *cis*-elimination does make the E_i mechanism seem predominant for these processes.

Little kinetic data is available *[391, 475]*, but the frequency factor is not far from normal ($\log_{10}A \sim 12.3$ to 12.7), and as the reaction can be calculated to be some 20 or 12 kcal.cal.mole^{-1} more exothermic than those of halides or esters the transition state would be expected to resemble the reactants more than in the other series which have been considered, and to involve less bond-making and -breaking. In most cases the products of decomposition of corresponding acetates and xanthates are similar (despite the difference in reaction conditions) *[458]*, but sometimes the Saytzeff rule applies to the pyrolyses of (not atypical) xanthates. The only kinetic-isotope data have been used for criteria between two possible gross mechanisms (*cf.* sect. 3) and cannot illuminate the rather obscure situation under discussion.

(d) Amine-oxides

No quantitative kinetic data are available for these even more exothermic processes. Product data *[52]* from compounds $R_1R_2\overset{+}{N}Me\overset{-}{O}$ have shown that the olefin distribution is almost statistical, and that α- and β-methylation have little influence on the rate of elimination from a particular branch: for instance, the rates from ethyl, isopropyl, and *tert*-butyl compounds can be estimated to be in the ratio $1:3:6$. These observations are consistent with only a small development of double bond character or of C_β–H or C_α–N breakage in the transition state—as would be expected from the exothermicity—and with a balance of individually small polar and steric effects. The only steric effects discernible are those between α- and β-linked substituents which lead to a predominance of *trans*- over *cis*-olefins when such isomerism is possible.

Phenyl substituents may favour more extensive double-bond formation, for elimination into the phenyl-substituted branch of $PhCH_2CH_2(\overset{+}{N}Me\overset{-}{O})CH_2CH_3$ is favoured by 70-fold over the alternative path. The relative rates of bimolecular elimination from β-phenylethyl and ethyl 'onium compounds in solution are 6,000 to 1, but a comparison with the analogous amine-oxides is unfair, for the 'onium degradation probably involves a two stage mechanism.

Recently it has been shown that amine oxides will decompose in dimethylsulphoxide at 25° [476]. This is the first example of an increase in basicity, caused by a change to a dipolar aprotic solvent, in an intra-molecular process.

6. Ion-pair and other Mechanisms

Some *trans*-elimination often occurs under conditions believed to be E_i. In his pioneer work on the Chugaev reaction, Huckel [27] found 20% of this orientation from the *trans*-decalyl-1-isomer; but probably his starting materials were impure for a more typical result is the 7% or 4% obtained from *cis*-2-phenylcyclohexyl acetates and xanthates [38]. Ester pyrolyses at elevated temperatures always yield the largest *trans*-percentages, and the milder Chugaev and Cope conditions give very little: for the last two reactions the *cis*-processes were favoured by factors of 9 and 30 respectively for 3-phenyl-2-butyl compounds [423, 424]. *trans*-Eliminations can only be detected in either conformationally fixed substrates or when geometrical isomers are formed, and so the incidence of these mechanisms in pyrolyses in general can only be speculated upon.

These unexpected processes could be due to heterolytic, radical, ion-pair, or radical-pair processes (in the last type the radicals formed by C–X fission do not separate); and some decompositions of sulphites [395, 459], chloroformates [394], borates [400], and sulphoxides [397], which are stereo-indiscriminate, may involve such mechanisms to a large or even exclusive degree. The formation of rearranged olefins from neopentyl halides [446] and chloroformates [393] indicates an ion-forming reaction.

Bornyl xanthate and benzoate decompose to form camphene, bornylene, and tricyclene [440]. The bornylene probably arises from a normal *cis*-process; but the camphene (and perhaps the tricyclene) must be the result of step-wise reaction with a loss of asymmetry* at some stage, for about 70% of the optical activity is destroyed. Isobornyl xanthate gives camphene with an almost complete retention of optical purity, and a concerted E_1 process with a 7-membered transition state (CXLII) is believed, for steric

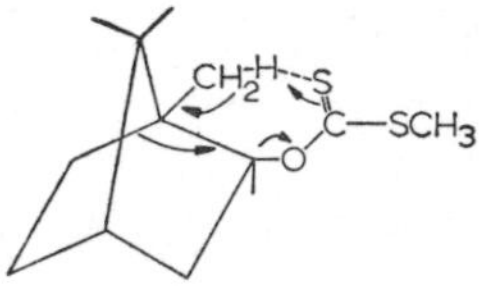

(CXLII)

reasons, to predominate here and also to appear in the other examples cited. A similar structure could also account for tricyclene formation. The corresponding benzoate, which is expected to have a much greater tendency to ionise, only gave camphene of low optical purity. The kinetically controlled unimolecular decomposition of bornyl chloride in the gas-phase also gave up to 75% rearranged products, but data concerning the optical properties of the products were not obtained [447].

In connection with these studies it is significant that although camphene, rather than the unrearranged bornylene, was obtained from the decompositions of isobornyltrimethylammonium salts in both neutral and strongly alkaline conditions; the olefin was only obtained in a state of high optical purity under the latter conditions [100]. This result could be due to ylide formation and the advent of an α'-β mechanism, formally similar to the postulated mechanism for xanthate decomposition, under the strongly basic conditions. In less basic media an E1 mechanism leading to a symmetrical synartetic ion must occur.

---

* Presumably through the formation of a symmetrical synartetic ion.

7. Other cis-Processes

The adducts from Diels-Alder reactions are often thermally unstable and especially endo-linked products formed from a cyclopen-
tadiene will readily decompose on warming, or at their melting
points [477] (reaction 122).

$$
\underset{\underset{\text{CH}}{\overset{\text{CH}}{\big|}}}{\overset{\underset{\text{CH}_2}{\overset{\text{CH}}{\diagdown}}}{\text{CH}}}
\quad \xrightarrow{\;\Delta H\;} \quad
\text{CH} \diagup \text{CH} \diagdown \text{CH}_2 + \text{CH} \diagup \text{CO} \diagdown \text{O}
\qquad (122)
$$

Studies of the condensation and the application of the principle
of microscopic reversibility should clarify the mechanism of this
cis-elimination, but the situation is at present obscure [478, 479].

Pyrolysis of cyclic olefins may produce a similar elimination, for
which the reverse condensation of the products is unknown. Thus
bornylene will decompose at 300° to form ethylene and 1,5,5-
trimethylcyclopenta-1,3-diene [480].

The mechanism of certain cis-eliminations of phosphorus-containing
compounds is also imperfectly understood [481]. The most important of these is the Wittig olefin synthesis (reaction 123) which

$$
\underset{\overset{\|}{O}}{-C-} + \bar{C}H_2-\overset{+}{P}Ph_3 \;\rightleftarrows\; \underset{\overset{|}{O}\;\overset{+}{P}Ph_3}{-C-CH_2} \;\longrightarrow\; -\overset{|}{C}=CH_2 + Ph_3\overset{+}{P}\cdot\bar{O}
\qquad (123)
$$

involves the adduct of a phosphonium ylide and a ketone [482].
This reaction is carried out under heterogeneous conditions in a
solvent favouring ion-pairing, and kinetic studies are hence difficult
to perform or to interpret.

REFERENCES

1. C. K. INGOLD, *Structure and Mechanism in Organic Chemistry*, Bell, London, 1953, Ch. 8.
2. W. HANHART AND C. K. INGOLD, *J. Chem. Soc.*, (1927) 997.
3. E. D. HUGHES, C. K. INGOLD *et al.*, *J. Chem. Soc.*, (1948) 2093 and previous papers.
4. S. ASPERGER, N. ILAKOVAC AND D. PAVLOVIC, *J. Am. Chem. Soc.*, 83 (1961) 5032.
5. V. J. SHINER, *J. Am. Chem. Soc.*, 74 (1952) 5285.
6. K. B. WIBERG, *Chem. Revs.*, 55 (1955) 713.
7. F. H. WESTHEIMER, *Chem. Revs.*, 61 (1961) 265.
8. W. H. SAUNDERS AND S. ASPERGER, *J. Am. Chem. Soc.*, 79 (1957) 1612.
9. E. BUNCEL AND A. N. BOURNS, *Can. J. Chem.*, 38 (1960) 2457.
10. E. D. HUGHES, C. K. INGOLD AND C. S. PATEL, *J. Chem. Soc.*, (1933) 526.
11. E. D. HUGHES, *J. Am. Chem. Soc.*, 57 (1935) 708.
12. E. D. HUGHES, C. K. INGOLD *et al.*, *J. Chem. Soc.*, (1940), 899.
13. I. DOSTOVSKY, E. D. HUGHES AND C. K. INGOLD, *J. Chem. Soc.*, (1946) 157 *et seq.*
14. E. D. HUGHES, C. K. INGOLD *et al.*, (a) *J. Chem. Soc.*, (1937) 1277; (b) *ibid.*, (1948) 2038; (c) *ibid.*, (1953) 3839; (d) *ibid.*, (1960) 4094.
15. A. R. HAWDON, E. D. HUGHES AND C. K. INGOLD, *J. Chem. Soc.*, (1952) 2499.
16. E. L. PURLEE AND R. W. TAFT, *J. Am. Chem. Soc.*, 78 (1956) 5807.
17. V. J. SHINER, (a) *J. Am. Chem. Soc.*, 75 (1953) 2925; (b) *ibid.*, 76 (1954) 1603.
18. E. S. LEWIS AND C. E. BOOZER, *J. Am. Chem. Soc.*, 76 (1954) 791, 794.
19. A. STREITWIESER *et al.*, *J. Am. Chem. Soc.*, 80 (1958) 2326.
20. L. S. BARTELL, *J. Am. Chem. Soc.*, 83 (1961) 3567.
21. S. WINSTEIN *et al.*, *J. Am. Chem. Soc.*, 74 (1952) 1120.
22. E. D. HUGHES, C. K. INGOLD *et al.*, *J. Chem. Soc.*, (1954) 642, 647, 2914, 2930.
23. V. GOLD, *J. Chem. Soc.*, (1956), 4633 and references therein.
24. E. D. HUGHES, C. K. INGOLD AND U. G. SHAPIRO, *J. Chem. Soc.*, (1936) 225.
25. C. A. BUNTON, *Substitution at a saturated Carbon Atom*, Elsevier, Amsterdam, 1963.
26. P. F. FRANKLAND, *J. Chem. Soc.*, (1912) 654.
27. W. HÜCKEL, W. TAPPE AND G. LEGUTKE, *Ann.*, 543 (1940) 191.
28. W. KLYNE AND V. PRELOG, *Experientia*, 16 (1960) 521.
29. D. J. CRAM, F. D. GREENE AND C. H. DePUY, *J. Am. Chem. Soc.* 78 (1956) 790.

30. S. WINSTEIN, D. PRESSMAN AND W. G. YOUNG, *J. Am. Chem. Soc.*, 61 (1939) 1645.
31. S. J. CRISTOL *et al.*, (a) *J. Am. Chem. Soc.*, 69 (1947) 338; (b) *ibid.*, 73 (1951) 674.
32. E. D. HUGHES, C. K. INGOLD AND R. PASTERNAK, *J. Chem. Soc.*, (1953) 3832.
33. S. J. CRISTOL AND N. L. HAUSE, *J. Am. Chem. Soc.*, 74 (1952) 2193.
34. D. V. BANTHORPE, E. D. HUGHES and C. K. INGOLD, *J. Chem. Soc.*, (1960) 4054.
35. S. WINSTEIN AND G. C. ROBINSON, *J. Am. Chem. Soc.*, 80 (1958) 169.
36. W. HÜCKEL *et al.*, *Ann.*, 477 (1930) 131.
37. G. VARON *et al.*, *Bull. soc. chim. France*, 49 (1931) 567, 937.
38. E. R. ALEXANDER AND A. MUDRAK, *J. Am. Chem. Soc.*, 72 (1950) 1810.
39. D. J. CRAM, *J. Am. Chem. Soc.*, 74 (1952) 2137.
40. A. C. CATCHPOLE, E. D. HUGHES AND C. K. INGOLD, *J. Chem. Soc.*, (1948) 8.
41. G. S. HAMMOND, *J. Am. Chem. Soc.*, 77 (1955) 334.
42. J. F. BUNNETT, *Angew. Chemie* (intern. ed.), 1 (1962) 228.
43. V. J. SHINER AND M. L. SMITH, (a) *J. Am. Chem. Soc.*, 80 (1958) 4095; (b) *ibid.*, 83 (1961) 593.
44. W. H. SAUNDERS AND D. H. EDISON, *J. Am. Chem. Soc.*, 82 (1960) 138.
45. R. P. BELL, *The Proton in Chemistry*, Methuen, London, 1959, Ch. 11.
46. M. S. SILVER, *J. Am. Chem. Soc.*, 83 (1961) 3487.
47. W. G. YOUNG, D. PRESSMAN AND C. D. CORYELL, *J. Am. Chem. Soc.*, 61 (1939) 1641.
48. D. J. CRAM AND F. A. ABD-ELHAFEZ, *J. Am. Chem. Soc.*, 74 (1952) 5851.
49. D. Y. CURTIN AND D. B. KELLOM, *J. Am. Chem. Soc.*, 75 (1953) 6011.
50. S. J. CRISTOL AND R. S. BLY, *J. Am. Chem. Soc.*, 82 (1960) 142.
51. H. J. LUCAS, T. P. SIMPSON AND J. M. CARTER, *J. Am. Chem. Soc.*, 47 (1925) 1465.
52. A. C. COPE *et al.*, *J. Am. Chem. Soc.*, 79 (1957) 4720.
53. H. C. BROWN AND O. H. WHEELER, *J. Am. Chem. Soc.*, 78 (1956) 2199.
54. T. THOMSON AND T. S. STEVENS, *J. Chem. Soc.*, (1932) 1932.
55. W. VON E. DOERING AND H. MEISLICH, *J. Am. Chem. Soc.*, 74 (1952) 2099.
56. E. R. TRUMBULL AND G. L. WILLETTE, quoted in ref. [242], p. 335.
57. H. C. BROWN AND M. NAKAGAWA, *J. Am. Chem. Soc.*, 77 (1955) 3614.

58. C. K. INGOLD, *Proc. Chem. Soc.*, (1962) 265.
59. A. ALLISON, C. BAMFORD AND J. H. RIDD, *Chem. & Ind.*, (1958) 718.
60. D. V. BANTHORPE, R. MORE O'FERRALL and J. H. RIDD forthcoming paper, in *J. Chem. Soc.*, 1963.
61. C. G. SWAIN AND C. B. SCOTT, *J. Am. Chem. Soc.*, 75 (1953) 141.
62a. A. J. PARKER, *Proc. Chem. Soc.*, (1961) 371.
62. A. J. PARKER, *J. Chem. Soc.*, (1961) 1328.
63. P. B. D. DE LA MARE AND C. A. VERNON, *J. Chem. Soc.*, (1956) 141.
64. E. L. ELIEL AND R. S. RO, *J. Am. Chem. Soc.*, 79 (1957) 5995; *Tetrahedron*, 2 (1958) 353.
65. C. W. SHOPPEE, H. C. RICHARDS AND C. H. R. SUMMER, *J. Chem. Soc.*, (1956) 4817.
66. J. F. BUNNETT et al., *Proc. Chem. Soc.*, (1961) 305; *J. Amer. Chem. Soc.*, 84 (1962) 1606.
67. L. N. OWEN et al., *J. Chem. Soc.*, (1950) 579 et seq.
68. J. HINE AND W. H. BRADER, *J. Am. Chem. Soc.*, 75 (1953) 3964.
69. E. R. TURNBULL et al., *Abstracts A.C.S. Meeting*, Chicago, Sept. 1958, p. 76P.
70. S. HÜNIG AND W. B. BARON, *Chem. Ber.*, 90 (1957) 395.
71. E. S. LEWIS AND M. R. C. SYMONS, *Quart. Revs.*, (*London*), (1958) 237.
72. J. MILLER AND A. J. PARKER, *J. Am. Chem. Soc.*, 83 (1961) 117.
73. S. D. ROSS AND M. M. LABES, *J. Am. Chem. Soc.*, 79 (1957) 4155.
74. N. KORNBLUM et al., *J. Am. Chem. Soc.*, 78 (1956) 1497, 4037.
75. D. V. BANTHORPE AND A. J. PARKER, unpublished experiments.
76. R. P. BELL, J. A. FENLEY AND J. R. HULETT, *Proc. Roy. Soc.* (*London*), A 235 (1956) 453.
77. A. L. HENNE AND T. MIDGELEY, *J. Am. Chem. Soc.*, 58 (1936) 882.
78. P. TARRANT, in P. SIMONS, *Fluorine Chemistry*, Acad. Press, N.Y., 1954, Ch. 4.
79. D. V. BANTHORPE, *Ph. D. Thesis*, London, 1958, and unpublished results.
80. W. BOCKEMULLER AND K. WIECHERT, in *Newer Methods of Preparative Organic Chemistry*, Interscience, N.Y., 1948, pp. 241, 336.
81. V. DESMEUX, *Bull. acad. roy. Belges*, 20 (1934) 457.
82. K. HOFMANN, *J. Am. Chem. Soc.*, 70 (1948) 2597.
83. W. T. MILLER, J. H. FRIED AND H. GOLDWHITE, *J. Am. Chem. Soc.*, 82 (1960) 3091.
84. V. PETROW et al., *J. Chem. Soc.*, (1956) 627, 1184; *ibid.*, (1958) 1334.
85. M. HAUPTSCHEIN AND R. E. OESTERLING, *J. Am. Chem. Soc.*, 82 (1960) 2868.
86. D. J. CRAM et al., (a) *J. Am. Chem. Soc.*, 74 (1952) 5828; (b) *ibid.*, 76 (1954) 28.

87. A. L. SOLOMON AND H. C. THOMAS, *J. Am. Chem. Soc.*, 72 (1950) 2028.
88. L. N. OWEN AND M. F. CLARK, *J. Chem. Soc.*, (1950) 2103, 2108.
89. C. A. VERNON, personal communication.
90. R. P. HOLYSZ, *J. Am. Chem. Soc.*, 75 (1953) 4432.
91. E. M. CHAMBERLAIN *et al.*, *J. Am. Chem. Soc.*, 79 (1957) 456.
92. N. L. WENDLER, D. TAUB AND H. KUO, *J. Am. Chem. Soc.*, 82, (1960) 5701.
93. N. H. CROMWELL AND D. N. KEVILL, *J. Am. Chem. Soc.*, 83 (1961) 3812; *Proc. Chem. Soc.*, (1961) 252.
94. P. G. STEVENS AND J. H. RICHMOND, *J. Am. Chem. Soc.*, 63 (1941) 3132.
95. A. M. LOVELACE, D. A. RAUSCH AND W. POSTELNEK, *Aliphatic Fluorine Compounds*, Reinhold, N.Y., 1958, p. 103.
96. D. J. CRAM *et al.*, *J. Am. Chem. Soc.*, 83 (1961) 3678.
97. H. MEERWEIN, quoted in HOUBEN-WEYL, *Methoden der Organischen Chemie*, Vol. 5 (4), 1960, p. 730.
98. J. VON BRAUN, W. TEUFFERT AND K. WEISSBACH, *Ann.*, 472 (1929) 121.
99. J. WEINSTOCK, *J. Org. Chem.*, 21 (1956) 540.
100. J. McKENNA AND J. B. SLINGER, *J. Chem. Soc.*, (1958) 2759.
101. H. R. SNYDER AND J. H. BREWSTER, *J. Am. Chem. Soc.*, 71 (1949) 291.
102. J. H. BREWSTER AND E. L. ELIEL, (a) *Org. Reactions*, 7 (1953) 105, (b) *ibid.*, p. 137.
103. R. G. PEARSON AND D. C. VOGELSONG, *J. Am. Chem. Soc.*, 80 (1958) 1048.
104. S. HÜNIG AND M. KIESSEL, *Chem. Ber.*, 91 (1958) 380.
105. S. WINSTEIN, D. DARWISH AND N. J. HOLNESS, *J. Am. Chem. Soc.*, 78 (1956) 2915.
106. C. H. DePUY AND C. A. BISHOP, *J. Am. Chem. Soc.*, 82 (1960) 2532.
107. W. HÜCKEL *et al.*, *Ann.*, 477 (1930) 143; *ibid.*, 533 (1937) 1.
108. M. F. CLARKE, L. N. OWEN AND P. A. ROBINS, *J. Chem. Soc.*, (1949) 315 *et seq.*
109. D. S. NOYCE, B. R. THOMAS AND B. N. BASTIAN, *J. Am. Chem. Soc.*, 82 (1960) 885.
110. A. STREITWIESER, *Chem. Revs.*, 56 (1956) 588.
111. S. WINSTEIN, S. SMITH AND D. DARWISH, *Tetrahedron Letters*, No. 16 (1959) 24.
112. M. PAILER AND L. BILEK, *Monatsh.*, 79 (1948) 135.
113. H. T. OPENSHAW, A. R. BATTERSBY *et al.*, *J. Chem. Soc.*, (1949) S59, 1174; *ibid.*, (1955) 2888.
114. W. H. SAUNDERS AND T. H. BROWNLEE, *Proc. Chem. Soc.*, (1961) 314.

115. S. WINSTEIN, E. GRUNWALD AND R. JONES, *J. Am. Chem. Soc.*, 73 (1951) 2700.
116. W. H. SAUNDERS, C. B. GIBBONS AND R. A. WILLIAMS, *J. Am. Chem. Soc.*, 80 (1958) 4099.
117. E. S. AMIS, *Kinetics of Chemical Change in Solution*, Macmillan, N.Y., 1949, Ch. 8.
118. R. A. CLEMENT AND M. R. RICE, *J. Am. Chem. Soc.*, 81 (1959) 326.
119. E. F. CALDIN AND G. LONG, *J. Chem. Soc.*, (1954) 3737.
120. B. D. ENGLAND AND R. E. BURNS, *Tetrahedron Letters*, No. 24 (1960) 1.
121. P. MAMALIS AND H. N. RYDON, *J. Chem. Soc.*, (1955) 1049.
122. N. B. CHAPMAN AND J. L. LEVY, *J. Chem. Soc.*, (1952) 1673.
123. For references to the earlier literature, see ref. [1,3].
124. H. B. HENBLEST, *Ann. Repts. on Progr. Chem. (Chem. Soc. London)*, 53 (1956) 135.
125. C. K. INGOLD AND C. C. N. VASS, *J. Chem. Soc.*, (1928) 3125.
126. C. K. INGOLD et al., *J. Chem. Soc.*, (1933) 533.
127. E. D. HUGHES, C. K. INGOLD AND G. A. MAW, *J. Chem. Soc.*, (1948) 2072.
128. E. D. HUGHES, C. K. INGOLD et al., *J. Chem. Soc.*, (1948) 2077.
129. E. D. HUGHES, C. K. INGOLD AND L. I. WOOLF, *J. Chem. Soc.*, (1948) 2084.
130. M. J. S. DEWAR AND H. S. SCHMEISING, *Tetrahedron*, 5 (1959) 166; 11 (1960) 96.
131. E. D. HUGHES AND C. K. INGOLD, *Trans. Faraday Soc.*, 37 (1941) 657.
132. S. C. J. OLIVIER AND A. P. WEBER, *Rec. trav. chim.*, 53 (1934) 1087, 1093.
133. C. H. DEPUY AND D. H. FROEMSDORF, *J. Am. Chem. Soc.*, 79 (1957) 3710.
134. W. H. SAUNDERS AND R. A. WILLIAMS, *J. Am. Chem. Soc.*, 79 (1957) 3712.
135. M. ANTEUNIS et al., *Bull. soc. chim. Belges*, 68 (1959) 344.
136. W. HÜCKEL, *Theoretical Principles of Organic Chemistry*, Vol. 1, Elsevier, Amsterdam, 1955, p. 780.
137. E. D. HUGHES, C. K. INGOLD et al., *J. Chem. Soc.*, (1955) 3200.
138. C. H. SCHRAMM, *Science*, 112 (1950) 367.
139. T. D. NEVITT AND G. S. HAMMOND, *J. Am. Chem. Soc.*, 76 (1954) 4124.
140. E. J. COREY, *J. Am. Chem. Soc.*, 76 (1954) 175.
141. H. C. BROWN AND R. S. FLETCHER, *J. Am. Chem. Soc.*, 72 (1950) 1223.
142. H. C. BROWN et al., (a) *J. Am. Chem. Soc.*, 77 (1955) 3607; *ibid.*, (b) p. 3610; (c) p. 3614; (d) p. 3619; (e) p. 3623.

143. V. J. SHINER, M. J. BUSKIN AND M. C. SMITH, *J. Am. Chem. Soc.*, 77 (1955) 5525.
144. C. N. HINSHELWOOD AND J. SHORTER, *J. Chem. Soc.*, (1949) 2412.
145. E. D. HUGHES, C. K. INGOLD AND V. J. SHINER, *J. Chem. Soc.*, (1953) 3827.
146. R. B. TURNER, D. E. NETTLETON AND M. PERELMAN, *J. Am. Chem. Soc.*, 80 (1958) 1430.
147. H. C. BROWN *et al.*, *J. Am. Chem. Soc.*, 79 (1957) 1897.
148. V. J. SHINER, *J. Am. Chem. Soc.*, 82 (1960) 2655.
149. S. J. CRISTOL, *J. Am. Chem. Soc.*, 71 (1949) 1894.
150. H. T. LUCAS AND C. W. GOULD, *J. Am. Chem. Soc.*, 64 (1942) 601.
151. H. C. BROWN *et al.*, (a) *J. Am. Chem. Soc.*, 78 (1956) 2190; *ibid.*, (b) p. 2193; (c) p. 2197; (d) p. 2199; (e) p. 2203.
152. P. A. S. SMITH AND S. FRANK, *J. Am. Chem. Soc.*, 74 (1952) 509.
153. W. H. JONES, *Science*, 118 (1953) 387.
154. W. H. SAUNDERS, S. R. FAHRENHOLTZ, AND J. P. LOWE, *Tetrahedron Letters*, No. 18 (1960) 1.
155. J. HINE AND P. B. LANGFORD, *J. Am. Chem. Soc.*, 78 (1956) 5002.
156. M. KOULKES, *Compt. rend.*, 241 (1955) 1789.
157. D. V. BANTHORPE AND E. D. HUGHES, *Bull. soc. chim. France*, (1960) 1373.
158. F. BECKER, *Z. Naturforsch.*, 15(b) (1960) 251.
159. S. MISUSHIMA, *The Structure of Molecules*, Acad. Press, N.Y., 1954.
160. C. R. HAUSER *et al.*, *J. Am. Chem. Soc.*, 76 (1954) 5129.
161. S. J. CRISTOL AND D. D. FIX, *J. Am. Chem. Soc.*, 75 (1953) 2647.
162. J. WEINSTOCK, R. G. PEARSON AND F. G. BORDWELL, *J. Am. Chem. Soc.*, 78 (1956) 3473.
163. J. HINE *et al.*, (a) *J. Am. Chem. Soc.*, 80 (1958) 4282; (b) *ibid.*, 79 (1957) 1406; (c) *ibid.*, 83 (1961) 1219; (d) *ibid.*, 78 (1956) 3337.
164. J. HINE *et al.*, *J. Am. Chem. Soc.*, 81 (1959) 1129, 1131, 6446; 82 (1960) 1398.
165. E. F. LANDAU, W. F. WHITMORE AND P. DOTY, *J. Am. Chem. Soc.*, 68 (1946) 816.
166. R. B. BERNSTEIN *et al.*, *J. Am. Chem. Soc.*, 77 (1955) 6201.
167. A. N. NESMEYANOV *et al.*, *Bull. Acad. Sci. U.S.S.R.*, (1959) 2119.
168. M. FITZGIBBON, *J. Chem. Soc.*, (1938) 1218.
169. R. E. LUTZ, D. F. HINKLEY AND R. H. JORDAN, *J. Am. Chem. Soc.*, 73 (1951) 4647.
170. J. HINE AND L. A. KAPLAN, *J. Am. Chem. Soc.*, 82 (1960) 2915.
171. A. L. HENNE AND J. B. HINKAMP, *J. Am. Chem. Soc.*, 67 (1945) 1195.
172. R. P. LINSTEAD, L. N. OWEN AND R. F. WEBB, *J. Chem. Soc.*, (1953) 1211, 1218, 1225.
173. H. BOHME AND P. HELLER, *Chem. Ber.*, 86 (1953) 443, 785.

174. P. S. SKELL AND J. H. MACNAMARA, *J. Am. Chem. Soc.*, 79 (1957) 85.
175. Y. ISKANDER AND Y. RIAD, *J. Chem. Soc.*, (1961) 223.
176. S. J. CRISTOL *et al.*, *J. Am. Chem. Soc.*, 67 (1945) 1494; *ibid.*, 74 (1952) 3333.
177. E. D. HUGHES AND C. K. INGOLD, *J. Chem. Soc.*, (1933) 523.
178. E. D. BERGMANN *et al.*, *Org. Reactions*, 10 (1959) 181.
179. E. M. HODNETT AND J. J. FLYNN, *J. Am. Chem. Soc.*, 79 (1957) 2300.
180. C. J. COLLINS AND P. LIETSKE, *J. Am. Chem. Soc.*, 81 (1959) 5379.
181. C. J. BJORK *et al.*, *J. Am. Chem. Soc.*, 75 (1953) 1988.
182. R. H. WILEY AND L. C. BEHR, *J. Am. Chem. Soc.*, 72 (1950) 1822.
183. F. F. BLICKE, *Org. Reactions*, 1 (1942) 303.
184. J. HINE AND P. B. LANGFORD, *J. Am. Chem. Soc.*, 79 (1957) 5497.
185. S. PATAI *et al.*, *J. Chem. Soc.*, (1962) 1741.
186. R. HUISGEN, in *Theoretical Organic Chemistry*, Butterworths, London, 1959, p. 158.
187. D. J. CRAM, *J. Am. Chem. Soc.*, 74 (1952) 2149.
188. D. D. EVANS AND C. W. SHOPPEE, *J. Chem. Soc.*, (1953) 540.
189. H. C. STEVENS AND O. GRUMMITT, *J. Am. Chem. Soc.*, 74 (1952) 4876.
190. H. L. GOERING AND H. H. ESPY, *J. Am. Chem. Soc.*, 78 (1956) 1454.
191. J. WEINSTOCK AND F. C. BORDWELL, *J. Am. Chem. Soc.*, 77 (1955) 6706.
192. S. J. CRISTOL AND F. R. STERMITZ, *J. Am. Chem. Soc.*, 82 (1960) 4692.
193. A. C. COPE, G. A. BERCHTOLD AND D. L. ROSS, *J. Am. Chem. Soc.* 83 (1961) 3859.
194. J. WEINSTOCK, R. G. PEARSON AND F. G. BORDWELL, *J. Am. Chem. Soc.*, 78 (1956) 3468, 3473.
195. F. G. BORDWELL AND M. L. PETERSON, *J. Am. Chem. Soc.*, 77 (1955) 1145.
196. H. L. GOERING, D. L. RELYEA AND K. L. HOWE, *J. Am. Chem. Soc.*, 79 (1957) 2502.
197. E. D. HUGHES AND J. C. MAYNARD, *J. Chem. Soc.*, (1960) 4087.
198. J. WEINSTOCK, J. L. BERNARD AND R. G. PEARSON, *J. Am. Chem. Soc.*, 80 (1958) 4961.
199. D. J. CRAM, D. A. SCOTT AND W. D. NIELSEN, *J. Am. Chem. Soc.*, 83 (1961) 3696.
200. F. G. BORDWELL AND P. S. LANDIS, *J. Am. Chem. Soc.*, 79 (1957) 1593.
201. C. J. COLLINS *et al.*, *J. Am. Chem. Soc.*, 79 (1957) 6160; *ibid.*, 83 (1961) 3654.

202. A. C. COPE AND D. L. ROSS, *J. Am. Chem. Soc.*, 83 (1961) 3854.
203. V. PETROW and D. N. KIRK, *J. Chem. Soc.*, (1958) 1334.
204. Y. POCKER, *Ann. Repts. on Progr. Chem.* (*Chem. Soc. London*), 54 (1959) 177.
205. C. K. INGOLD *et al.*, *J. Chem. Soc.*, (1930) 713; (1933) 69.
206. W. VON E. DOERING AND A. K. HOFFMANN, *J. Am. Chem. Soc.*, 77 (1955) 521.
207. F. WEYGARD, H. DANIEL AND H. SIMON, *Chem. Ber.*, 91 (1958) 1691; Ann. 654 (1962) 111.
208. C. W. CRANE AND H. N. RYDON, *J. Chem. Soc.*, (1947) 766.
209. S. J. CRISTOL AND R. F. HELMREICH, *J. Am. Chem. Soc.*, 77 (1955) 5034.
210. C. R. HAUSER *et al.*, *J. Am. Chem. Soc.*, 74 (1952) 5599; *ibid.*, 81 (1959) 2784.
211. R. L. LETSINGER *et al.*, *J. Am. Chem. Soc.*, 75 (1953) 2649; *ibid.*, 78 (1956) 6079.
212. P. AMAGAT, *Bull. soc. chim. France*, 49 (1931) 1410.
213. C. R. HAUSER *et al.*, *J. Am. Chem. Soc.*, 69 (1947) 587.
214. C. R. HAUSER, *J. Am. Chem. Soc.*, 62 (1940) 933.
215. S. J. CRISTOL AND R. S. BLY, *J. Am. Chem. Soc.*, 83 (1961) 4027.
216. C. G. SWAIN AND E. R. THORNTON, *J. Am. Chem. Soc.*, 83 (1961) 4033.
217. V. FRANZEN *et al.*, *Chem. Ber.*, 94 (1961) 2942.
218. W. KIRMSE AND W. VON E. DOERING, *Tetrahedron*, 11 (1960) 266.
219. L. FRIEDMAN AND J. G. BERGER, *J. Am. Chem. Soc.*, 83 (1961) 492, 500.
220. L. FREIDMAN AND H. SHECHTER, *J. Am. Chem. Soc.*, 81 (1959) 5513.
221. C. H. DEPUY AND D. H. FROEMSDORF, *J. Am. Chem. Soc.*, 82 (1960) 634.
222. M. C. WHITING AND J. W. POWELL, *Tetrahedron*, 12 (1961) 168.
223. C. H. LANGFORD AND R. L. BURWELL, *J. Am. Chem. Soc.*, 82 (1960) 1504.
224. G. WITTIG *et al.*, (a) *Ann.*, 599 (1956) 13; (b) *ibid.*, 612 (1958) 102; (c) *ibid.*, 632 (1960) 85.
225. J. RABIANT AND G. WITTIG, *Bull. soc. chim. France*, (1957) 798.
226. A. C. COPE *et al.*, *J. Am. Chem. Soc.*, 75 (1953) 3212; 84 (1962) 2411.
227. A. C. COPE *et al.*, *J. Am. Chem. Soc.*, 83 (1961) 3861.
228. V. FRANZEN AND C. MERTZ, *Chem. Ber.*, 93 (1960) 2819; *ibid.*, 94 (1961) 2937.
229. W. H. SAUNDERS AND D. PAVLOVIC, *Chem. & Ind.*, (1962) 180.
230. G. AYREY, E. BUNCEL AND A. N. BOURNS, *Proc. Chem. Soc.*, (1961) 458.
231. S. J. CRISTOL, W. BARASCH AND C. H. TIEMAN, *J. Am. Chem. Soc.*, 77 (1955) 583.

232. R. B. CLAYTON, H. B. HENBLEST AND M. SMITH, *J. Chem. Soc.*, (1957) 1982.
233. P. KARRER *et al.*, *Helv. Chim. Acta*, 38 (1955) 1067.
234. *Cf.* P. B. D. DE LA MARE, *Ann. Repts. on Progr. Chem.* (*Chem. Soc. London*), 47 (1950)142; G. BADDELEY, *ibid.*, 51 (1954) 159.
235. C. BUMGARDNER, *J. Am. Chem. Soc.*, 83 (1961) 4420, 4423.
236. V. PRELOG, *Angew. Chem.*, 70 (1958) 145, and references therein.
237. R. A. RAPHAEL, *Proc. chem. Soc.*, (1962) 97.
238. C. A. GROB, in *Theoretical Organic Chemistry*, Butterworths, London, 1959, p. 114.
239. C. A. GROB, *Bull. soc. chim. France*, (1960) 1360.
240. F. C. WHITMORE *et al.*, *J. Am. Chem. Soc.*, 76 (1954) 1613.
241. A. G. BROOK AND H. GILMAN, *J. Am. Chem. Soc.*, 77 (1955) 2322.
242. A. C. COPE AND E. R. TRUMBULL, *Org. Reactions*, 11 (1960) 317.
243. K. W. BENTLEY, *The Alkaloids*, Acad. Press, N.Y., 1957, pp. 119, 176 *et seq.*
244. A. C. COPE *et al.*, *J. Am. Chem. Soc.*, 79 (1957) 4729; *J. Org. Chem.*, 27 (1962) 2627.
245. A. FEER AND W. KOENIGS, *Ber.*, 18 (1885) 2388.
246. M. MOELLER, *Ann.*, 242 (1887) 313.
247. K. FUJISE, *Sci. Papers Inst. Phys. Chem. Research* (*Tokio*), 9 (1928) 91.
248. R. ROBINSON *et al.*, *J. Chem. Soc.*, (1934) 581; *ibid.*, (1935) 1685.
249. D. H. R. BARTON AND R. C. COOKSON, *Quart. Revs.* (*London*), 10 (1956) 44.
250. W. KLYNE, in *Progress in Stereochemistry*, Vol. 1, Butterworths, London, 1954, Ch. 2.
251. H. D. ORLOFF, *Chem. Revs.*, 54 (1954) 347.
252. S. WINSTEIN AND N. J. HOLNESS, *J. Am. Chem. Soc.*, 77 (1955) 5562.
253. N. B. CHAPMAN AND R. E. PARKER, *J. Chem. Soc.*, (1960) 3634.
254. B. CROSS AND G. H. WHITHAM, *J. Chem. Soc.*, (1960) 3892.
255. E. D. HUGHES AND J. WILBY, *J. Chem. Soc.*, (1960) 4094.
256. E. D. HUGHES, C. K. INGOLD AND J. B. ROSE, *J. Chem. Soc.*, (1953) 3839.
257. S. WINSTEIN *et al.*, *J. Am. Chem. Soc.*, 74 (1952) 1127.
258. A. C. COPE AND E. M. ACTON, *J. Am. Chem. Soc.*, 80 (1958) 355.
259. V. J. SHINER, *J. Am. chem. Soc.*, 82 (1960) 2655.
260. H. L. GOERING AND R. L. REEVES, *J. Am. Chem. Soc.*, 78 (1956) 4931.
261. D. Y. CURTIN, R. D. STOLOW AND W. MAYA, *J. Am. Chem. Soc.*, 81 (1959) 3330.
262. N. L. MCNIVEN AND J. READ, *J. Chem. Soc.*, (1952) 159.
263. R. D. HAWORTH, J. MCKENNA AND R. G. POWELL, *J. Chem. Soc.*, (1953) 1110.

264. D. H. R. BARTON *e al.*, *J. Am. Chem. Soc.*, 72 (1950) 1066; *J. Chem. Soc.*, (1951) 1048.
265. B. B. GENT AND J. McKENNA, *J. Chem. Soc.*, (1959) 137.
266. A. C. COPE, P. T. MOORE AND W. R. MOORE, *J. Am. Chem. Soc.*, 81 (1959) 3153; 82 (1960) 1744.
267. A. C. COPE, D. C. McLEAN AND N. A. NELSON, *J. Am. Chem. Soc.*, 77 (1955) 1628; 82 (1960) 1744.
268. K. ZIEGLER AND H. WILMS, *Ann.*, 567 (1950) 1.
269. A. C. COPE AND C. L. BUMGARDNER, *J. Am. Chem. Soc.*, 78 (1956) 2812.
270. K. JEWERS AND J. McKENNA, *J. Chem. Soc.*, (1958) 2209.
271. R. B. TURNER AND R. H. CANNER, *J. Am. Chem. Soc.*, 79 (1957) 253.
272. A. C. COPE *et al.*, *J. Am. Chem. Soc.*, 82 (1960) 1750.
273. J. McKENNA, *Chem. & Ind.*, (1954) 406; *J. Chem. Soc.*, (1960) 1575.
274. H. WIELAND, C. SCHOPF AND W. HERMSER, *Ann.*, 444 (1925) 40.
275. C. SCHOPF AND E. BOETTCHER, *Ann.*, 448 (1926) 1.
276. F. E. KING *et al.*, *J. Chem. Soc.*, (1953) 250.
277. H. BOOTH AND F. E. KING, *J. Chem. Soc.*, (1958) 2688.
278. F. S. FAWCETT, *Chem. Revs.*, 47 (1950) 219.
279. W. VON E. DOERING AND E. F. SCHOENEWALDT, *J. Am. Chem. Soc.*, 73 (1951) 2333.
280. S. J. CRISTOL AND E. F. HOEGGER, *J. Am. Chem. Soc.*, 79 (1957) 3438.
281. A. C. COPE, E. CIGANEK AND N. A. LEBEL, *J. Am. Chem. Soc.*, 81 (1959) 2799.
282. G. A. GROB, H. KNY AND A. GAGNEUX, *Helv. Chim. Acta*, 40 (1957) 130.
283. S. J. CRISTOL AND R. P. ARGANBRIGHT, *J. Am. Chem. Soc.*, 79 (1957) 3441.
284. S. J. CRISTOL, F. R. STERMITZ AND P. S. RAMSEY, *J. Am. Chem. Soc.*, 78 (1956) 4939.
285. P. B. D. DE LA MARE, N. V. KLASSEN AND R. KOENIGSBERGER, *J. Chem. Soc.*, (1961) 5285.
286. L. RUZICKA *et al.*, *Helv. Chim. Acta*, 3 (1920) 756; 4 (1921) 666; 7 (1924) 489.
287. J. L. SIMONSON, *The Terpenes*, Vol. 2, 2nd. Edition, Cambridge Univ. Press, London, 1949, p. 11.
288. S. WINSTEIN *et al.*, *J. Am. Chem. Soc.*, 81 (1959) 6523, 6524.
289. W. M. SCHUBERT *et al.*, (a) *J. Am. Chem. Soc.*, 74 (1952) 4590, (b) *ibid.*, 77 (1955) 5755.
290. W. G. YOUNG, S. J. CRISTOL AND T. SKEI, *J. Am. Chem. Soc.*, 65 (1943) 2099.
291. H. O. HOUSE AND R. S. RO, *J. Am. Chem. Soc.*, 80 (1958) 182.
292. T. ALFREY *et al.*, *J. Am. Chem. Soc.*, 74 (1952) 2097.

293. J. WEINSTOCK, F. N. LEWIS AND F. G. BORDWELL, *J. Am. Chem. Soc.*, 78 (1956) 6072.
294. S. J. CRISTOL AND L. E. RADEMACHER, *J. Am. Chem. Soc.*, 81 (1959) 1600.
295. D. R. JAMES, R. W. REES AND C. W. SHOPPEE, *J. Chem. Soc.*, (1955) 1370.
296. J. W. CORNFORTH, R. H. CORNFORTH AND K. MATHEW, *J. Chem. Soc.*, (1959) 112.
297. L. F. FIESER, *J. Am. Chem. Soc.*, 75 (1953) 5421.
298. R. DULOC et al., *Compt. rend.*, 242 (1956) 1184.
299. W. M. SCHUBERT AND S. M. LEAHY, *J. Am. Chem. Soc.*, 79 (1957) 381.
300. J. HINE AND W. H. BRADER, *J. Am. Chem. Soc.*, 77 (1955) 361.
301. S. J. CRISTOL, J. Q. WEBER AND M. C. BRINDELL, *J. Am. Chem. Soc.*, 78 (1956) 598.
302. H. L. GOERING AND H. H. ESPY, *J. Am. Chem. Soc.*, 77 (1955) 5023.
303. S. J. ANGYAL AND R. J. YOUNG, *Aus r. J. Chem.*, 14 (1961) 8.
304. T. L. JACOBS, *Org. Reactions*, 5 (1949) 1.
305. S. J. CRISTOL et al., (a) *J. Am. Chem. Soc.*, 76 (1954) 3005; (b) *ibid.*, 4558.
306. S. I. MILLER et al., *J. Am. Chem. Soc.*, 74 (1952) 629; *J. Org. Chem.* 76 (1961) 2619.
307. S. J. CRISTOL AND A. BEGOON, *J. Am. Chem. Soc.*, 74 (1952) 5025.
308. A. MICHEAL, *J. prakt. Chem.*, 52 (1895) 308.
309. K. E. HARWELL AND L. F. HATCH, *J. Am. Chem. Soc.*, 77 (1955) 1682.
310. W. R. VAUGHAN AND R. L. CRAVEN, *J. Am. Chem. Soc.*, 77 (1955) 4629.
311. S. J. CRISTOL AND W. P. NORRIS, *J. Am. Chem. Soc.*, 75 (1953) 632, 2645.
312. E. GROVENSTEIN AND D. E. LEE, *J. Am. Chem. Soc.*, 75 (1953) 2639.
313. J. CASTRO, *J. Am. Chem. Soc.*, 72 (1950) 5311.
314. G. OHLOFF, *Ann.*, 627 (1959) 79.
315. P. LIMA, *Diss. Abstr.*, 26 (1959) 499.
316. F. C. WHITMORE et al., *J. Am. Chem. Soc.*, 55 (1933) 3732.
317. I. DOSTOVSKY AND F. S. KLEIN, *J. Chem. Soc.*, (1955) 4401.
318. J. MANASSEN AND F. S. KLEIN, *J. Chem. Soc.*, (1960) 4203.
319. C. A. BUNTON AND D. R. LLEWELLYN, *J. Chem. Soc.*, (1957) 3402.
320. I. DOSTOVSKY AND F. S. KLEIN, *J. Chem. Soc.*, (1955) 791.
321. E. GRUNWALD, A. HELLER AND F. S. KLEIN, *J. Chem. Soc.*, (1957) 2604.
322. R. W. TAFT et al., *J. Am. Chem. Soc.*, 77 (1955) 1584.
323. R. W. TAFT et al., *J. Am. Chem. Soc.*, 82 (1960) 4729.
324. L. MELANDER AND P. C. MHYRE, *Arkiv Kemi*, 13 (1959) 507.

325. G. S. HAMMOND et al., J. Am. Chem. Soc., 76 (1954) 4121; 82 (1960) 4323.
326. J. ROCEK, Collection Czechoslov. Chem. Communs., 25 (1960) 375.
327. M. J. S. DEWAR, in Theoretical Organic Chemistry, Butterworths, London, 1959, p. 179.
328. L. G. CANNELL AND R. W. TAFT, J. Am. Chem. Soc., 78 (1956) 5812.
329. W. A. MOSLER AND J. C. COX, J. Am. Chem. Soc., 72 (1950) 3701.
330. P. IKEDA AND F. FUJITA, Bull. Inst. Chem. Research Kyoto Univ., 7 (1928) 257.
331. J. L. SIMONSEN, The Terpenes, Vol. 2, Cambridge, 1949, p. 349 et seq.
332. G. M. GUTMAN AND W. J. HICKINBOTHAM, J. Chem. Soc., (1951) 3344.
333. J. L. SIMONSEN, The Terpenes, Vol. 1, Cambridge, 1947, p. 256 et seq.
334. C. C. PRICE AND J. V. KARABINAS, J. Am. Chem. Soc., 62 (1940) 1159.
335. H. SCHAEFFER AND C. J. COLLINS, J. Am. Chem. Soc., 78 (1956) 124.
336. H. L. GOERING, R. L. REEVES AND H. H. ESPY, J. Am. Chem. Soc., 78 (1956) 4926.
337. P. D. BARTLETT, in H. GILMAN, Organic Chemistry, Vol. 3, Wiley, N.Y., 1953, p. 51.
338. Ref. [333], p. 238 et seq.
339. H. HEUSNER, W. WAHRA AND F. WINTERNITZ, Helv. Chim. Acta, 37 (1954) 1052.
340. C. W. SHOPPEE AND G. H. R. SUMMERS, J. Chem. Soc., (1952) 1787.
341. D. H. R. BARTON, A. S. CAMPUS-NEVES AND R. C. COOKSON, J. Chem. Soc., (1956) 3500.
342. R. R. SAUERS, J. Am. Chem. Soc., 81 (1959) 4873.
343. R. R. SAUERS AND J. M. LANDESBURG, J. Org. Chem., 26 (1961) 964.
344. S. J. ANGYAL, Quart. Revs. (London), 11 (1957) 212.
345. R. B. TURNER AND R. B. WOODWARD, in R. MANSKE AND H. HOLMES, The Alkaloids, Vol. 3, Acad. Press, N.Y., 1956 p. 9.
346. Discussions Faraday Soc., 1950; G. C. BIRD, Ann. Repts. on Progr. Chem. (Chem. Soc. London), 51 (1954) 100.
347. M. E. WINFIELD, in P. H. EMMETT's, Catalysis, Vol. 7, Reinhold, N.Y., 1960, p. 93.
348. H. ADKINS AND S. H. WATKINS, J. Am. Chem. Soc., 73 (1951) 2184.
349. L. BERANAK et al., Collection Czechoslov. Chem. Communs., 25 (1960) 2513.
350. H. PINES et al., J. Am. Chem. Soc., 83 (1961) 2847, 3270, 3274.
351. A. C. ANDREWS AND J. S. CANTWELL, J. Phys. Chem., 65 (1961) 1089.
352. E. D. HUGHES, C. K. INGOLD AND J. H. RIDD, J. Chem. Soc., (1958) 58 et seq.

353. A. Streitwieser, *J. Org. Chem.*, 22 (1957) 861.
354. Houben-Weyl, *Methoden der Organischen Chemie*, Vol. 11 (2), 1958, p. 158.
355. J. D. Roberts *et al.*, *J. Am. Chem. Soc.*, 75 (1953) 5759; 77 (1955) 5558.
356. J. D. Roberts, R. E. McMahon and J. Hine, *J. Am. Chem. Soc.*, 72 (1950) 4237.
357. J. D. Roberts *et al.*, *J. Am. Chem. Soc.*, 74 (1952) 4283.
358. C. C. Lee, C. P. Slater and J. W. T. Spinks, *Can. J. Chem.*, 35 (1957) 1416.
359. P. A. Smith and D. R. Baer, *Org. Reactions*, 11 (1960) 157.
360. W. G. Dauben and J. B. Rogan, *J. Am. Chem. Soc.*, 79 (1957) 5002.
361. D. J. Cram and J. E. McCarty, *J. Am. Chem. Soc.*, 79 (1957) 2866.
362. J. E. Burr and L. S. Ciereszko, *J. Am. Chem. Soc.*, 74 (1952) 5431.
363. D. Y. Curtin and M. C. Crew, *J. Am. Chem. Soc.*, 76 (1954) 3719.
364. J. D. Roberts *et al.*, *J. Am. Chem. Soc.*, 76 (1954) 4501; 78 (1956) 584.
365. J. D. Roberts and R. H. Mazur, *J. Am. Chem. Soc.*, 73 (1951) 2509.
366. D. Semenow, C. H. Shih and W. C. Young, *J. Am. Chem. Soc.*, 80 (1958) 5472.
367. J. D. Roberts *et al.*, *J. Am. Chem. Soc.*, 83 (1961) 3670.
368. A. Streitwieser and W. D. Shaeffer, *J. Am. Chem. Soc.*, 79 (1957) 2888.
369. S. Burgess, *Ph.D. Thesis*, London, 1953.
370. J. A. Mills, *J. Chem. Soc.*, (1953) 260.
371. A. K. Bose, *Experientia*, 9 (1953) 256.
372. W. G. Dauben *et al.*, *J. Am. Chem. Soc.*, 76 (1954) 4420, 4426; 77 (1955) 48.
373. A. Stoll *et al.*, *Helv. Chim. Acta*, 37 (1954) 2039.
374. W. Hückel and R. Kupka, *Chem. Ber.*, 89 (1956) 1694.
375. W. Hückel and W. Ude, *Chem. Ber.*, 94 (1961) 1026.
376. A. Streitwieser and C. E. Coverdale, *J. Am. Chem. Soc.*, 81 (1959) 4275.
377. W. Hückel *et al.*, *Ann.*, 528 (1937) 57; 625 (1959) 1.
378. W. Hückel *et al.*, *Ber.*, 80 (1947) 39; *Ann.*, 585 (1954) 182.
379. J. A. Berson and D. Ben Efraim, *J. Am. Chem. Soc.*, 81 (1959) 4094.
380. J. D. Roberts *et al.*, *J. Am. Chem. Soc.*, 76 (1954) 4501.
381. P. D. Bartlett and L. H. Knox, *J. Am. Chem. Soc.*, 61 (1939) 3184.
382. C. W. Shoppee *et al.*, *J. Chem. Soc.*, (1957) 97, 4364; (1959) 345; (1961) 1583.

383. A. T. Austin and J. Howard, *J. Chem. Soc.*, (1961) 3281.
384. P. D. Bartlett, in H. Gilman, *Organic Chemistry*, Vol. 3, Wiley, N.Y., 1953, p. 45.
385. C. H. DePuy and R. W. King, *Chem. Revs.*, 60 (1960) 431.
386. J. L. Holmes and A. Maccoll, *Proc. Chem. Soc.*, (1957) 175.
387. E. D. Hughes and C. K. Ingold, *Quart. Revs. (London)*, 6 (1952) 34.
388. C. G. Swain, R. A. Wiles and R. F. Bader, *J. Am. Chem. Soc.*, 83 (1961) 1945.
389. H. E. Baumgarten and R. A. Setterquist, *J. Am. Chem. Soc.*, 79 (1957) 2605.
390. G. M. Calhoun and R. L. Burwell, *J. Am. Chem. Soc.*, 77 (1955) 6441.
391. G. L. O'Conner and H. R. Nace, *J. Am. Chem. Soc.*, 74 (1952) 5454; 75 (1953) 2118.
392. H. R. Nace, *J. Am. Chem. Soc.*, 81 (1959) 5428.
393. E. S. Lewis and C. E. Boozer, *J. Am. Chem. Soc.*, 74 (1952) 308.
394. E. S. Lewis and W. C. Herndon, *J. Am. Chem. Soc.*, 83 (1961) 1955, 1959, 1961.
395. C. C. Price and G. Berti, *J. Am. Chem. Soc.*, 76 (1954) 1207, 1211, 1213.
396. R. Dulou, G. Quesnell and M. de Bolton, *Bull. soc. chim. France*, (1959) 1340.
397. C. A. Kingsbury and D. J. Cram, *J. Am. Chem. Soc.*, 82 (1960) 1810.
398. E. M. La Combe and B. Stewart, *J. Am. Chem. Soc.*, 83 (1961) 3457.
399. K. A. Wilde, *J. Phys. Chem.*, 61 (1957) 385.
400. P. Lancecette, *Can. J. Chem.*, 40 (1962) 1471.
401. W. A. Bailey and C. N. Bird, *J. Org. Chem.*, 23 (1958) 996.
402. H. E. Baumgarten and R. A. Setterquist, *J. Am. Chem. Soc.*, 81 (1959) 2132.
403. C. Harries and M. Johnson, *Ber.*, 38 (1905) 1832.
404. J. W. Cook et al., *J. Chem. Soc.*, (1944) 322, (1949) 1074.
405. C. G. Swain et al., *J. Am. Chem. Soc.*, 83 (1961) 1951.
406. M. Szarc and J. Murawski, *Trans. Faraday Soc.*, 47 (1951) 269.
407. A. T. Blades et al., *Can. J. Chem.*, (1953) 31, 418; *J. Am. Chem. Soc.*, 74 (1952) 1039.
408. J. A. Barnard, *Trans. Faraday Soc.*, 55 (1959) 947.
409. H. O. Pritchard et al., *J. Chem. Soc.*, (1954) 546.
410. A. Maccoll and M. N. Kale, *J. Chem. Soc.*, (1957) 5020.
411. A. Maccoll and P. J. Thomas, *J. Chem. Soc.*, (1955) 979.
412. K. E. Howlett et al., *J. Chem. Soc.*, (1952) 3695, 4487, (1956) 3092.
413. D. H. R. Barton et al., *J. Chem. Soc.*, (1951) 2039 and preceding papers.

414. A. MACCOLL et al., J. Chem. Soc., (1960) 184 and 13 preceding papers.
415. A. MACCOLL et al., J. Chem. Soc., (1955) 2445; (1957) 5033; (1958) 3016; (1959) 1197.
416. A. MACCOLL, J. Chem. Soc., (1955) 965.
417. A. MACCOLL, in Theoretical Organic Chemistry, Butterworths, London, 1959, p. 230.
418. A. MACCOLL, J. Chem. Soc., (1958) 3398.
419. J. B. PERI AND F. DANIELS, J. Am. Chem. Soc., 72 (1950) 424.
420. H. R. NACE, D. MANLY, AND S. FUSCO, J. Org. Chem., 23 (1958) 687.
421. C. D. HURD AND F. H. BLUNCK, J. Am. Chem. Soc., 60 (1938) 2419.
422. R. F. BADER AND A. N. BOURNS, Can. J. Chem., 39 (1961) 348.
423. D. J. CRAM, J. Am. Chem. Soc., 71 (1949) 3883.
424. D. J. CRAM AND T. E. McCARTY, J. Am. Chem. Soc., 76 (1954) 5740.
425. D. H. R. BARTON, J. Chem. Soc., (1949) 2174.
426. G. R. ALEXANDER AND A. MUDRAK, J. Am. Chem. Soc., 72 (1950) 3194; 73 (1951) 59.
427. S. J. ANGYAL AND C. G. MacDONALD, J. Chem. Soc., (1952) 686.
428. W. J. BAILEY AND L. NICHOLAS, J. Org. Chem., 21 (1956) 854.
429. C. H. DePUY AND R. W. KING, J. Am. Chem. Soc., 83 (1961) 2743.
430. F. G. BORDWELL and P. S. LANDIS, J. Am. Chem. Soc., 80 (1958) 2450.
431. C. H. DePUY et al., J. Am. Chem. Soc., 81 (1959) 643.
432. N. C. McNIVEN AND J. READ, J. Chem. Soc., (1952) 2067.
433. D. H. R. BARTON, A. J. HEAD AND R. J. WILLIAMS, J. Chem. Soc., (1952) 453.
434. A. T. BLOMQUIST et al., (a) J. Am. Chem. Soc., 77 (1955) 1001, 6399; (b) ibid., 79 (1957) 3505.
435. A. C. COPE et al., J. Am. Chem. Soc., 82 (1960) 4663.
436. A. C. COPE AND N. A. LEBEL, J. Am. Chem. Soc., 82 (1960) 4656.
437. W. J. BAILEY AND C. N. BIRD, A. C. S. Meeting, Miami, April 1957, 44-0.
438. K. BENTLEY, J. C. BALL, AND J. P. RINGE, J. Chem. Soc., (1956) 1963.
439. G. C. OVERBERGER AND A. E. BORCHERT, J. Am. Chem. Soc., 82 (1960) 1007.
440. C. A. BUNTON, D. WHITTAKER AND K. KHALEELUDDIN, Nature, (1961) 715.
441. P. J. THOMAS, J. Chem. Soc., (1961) 136.
442. A. T. BLADES, Can. J. Chem., 36 (1958) 1043.
443. C. K. INGOLD, Proc. Chem. Soc., (1957) 279.
444. A. MACCOLL AND R. H. STONE, J. Chem. Soc., (1961) 2756.
445. C. H. DePUY, C. A. BISHOP AND G. N. GOEDERS, J. Am. Chem. Soc., 83 (1961) 2151.
446. A. MACCOLL AND G. S. SWINBOURNE, Proc. Chem. Soc., (1960) 409.

447. A. MACCOLL AND R. BICKNELL, *Chem. & Ind.*, (1961) 1912.
448. A. MACCOLL AND V. R. STIMSON, *J. Chem. Soc.*, (1960) 2836.
449. W. J. BAILEY AND W. F. HALE, *J. Am. Chem. Soc.*, 81 (1959) 647.
450. W. J. BAILEY AND J. J. HEWITT, *J. Org. Chem.*, 21 (1956) 543.
451. G. G. SMITH AND W. H. WETZEL, *J. Am. Chem. Soc.*, 79 (1957) 875.
452. A. T. BLADES AND P. W. GILDERSON, *Can. J. Chem.*, 38 (1960), 1401, 1407.
453. C. H. DePUY, R. W. KING AND D. H. FROEMSDORF, *Tetrahedron*, 7 (1959) 123.
454. C. H. DePUY AND R. E. LEARY, *J. Am. Chem. Soc.*, 79 (1957) 3705.
455. A. MACCOLL AND E. U. EMOVAN, *J. Chem. Soc.*, (1962) 335.
456. W. J. BAILEY *et al.*, *J. Org. Chem.*, 21 (1956) 36, 648, 854, 859.
457. G. G. SMITH, F. D. BAGLEY AND R. TAYLOR, *J. Am. Chem. Soc.*, 83 (1961) 3647.
458. R. A. BENESKER AND J. J. HAZDRA, *J. Am. Chem. Soc.*, 81 (1959) 5374.
459. F. C. BORDWELL AND P. S. LANDIS, *J. Am. Chem. Soc.*, 80 (1958) 6379, 6383.
460. W. G. LEE AND S. I. MILLER, *J. Phys. Chem.*, 66 (1962) 655.
461. R. F. HUDSON, *Chimia (Switz.)*, 16 (1962) 173.
462. L. RAND *et al.*, *J. Org. Chem.*, 27 (1962) 1034.
463. J. M. SPRAGUE AND T. B. JOHNSON, *J. Amer. Chem. Soc.*, 59 (1937) 1837.
464. A. J. BERLIN AND F. R. JANSEN, *Chem. and Ind.*, (1960) 998.
465. C. A. GROB *et al.*, *Tetrahedron Letters*, no. 1 (1962) 25.
466. C. M. STIRLING, *Chem. and Ind.*, (1960) 933.
467. C. PAPATHASSIOUS, *Diss. Abstrs.*, 22 (1962) 3406.
468. J. HINE AND O. B. RAMSAY, *J. Amer. Chem. Soc.*, 84 (1962) 973.
469. C. H. DePUY *et al.*, *J. Amer. Chem. Soc.*, 84 (1962) 1314.
470. A. C. COPE AND M. J. YOUNGQUIST, *J. Amer. Chem. Soc.*, 84 (1962) 2411.
471. S. J. CRISTOL AND D. DAVIES, *J. Org. Chem.*, 27 (1962) 293.
472. E. R. TRUMBULL *et al.*, *J. Org. Chem.*, 27 (1962) 2339.
473. E. VON RUDLOFF, *Canad. J. Chem.*, 39 (1961) 1.
474. W. J. BAILEY, *J. Org. Chem.*, 27 (1962) 1851.
475. H. R. NACE, *Org. Reacts.*, 12 (1962) 57.
476. D. J. CRAM *et al.*, *J. Amer. Chem. Soc.*, 84 (1962) 1734.
477. M. C. KLOETZEL, *Org. Reacts.*, 4 (1948) 1.
478. L. J. ANDREWS AND R. M. KEEFER, *J. Amer. Chem. Soc.*, 77 (1955) 6284.
479. J. A. BERSON, R. D. REYNOLDS AND W. H. JONES, *J. Amer. Chem. Soc.*, 78 (1956) 6049.
480. R. C. BICKNELL, *Ph. D. Thesis*, London, 1962.
481. J. I. G. CADOGAN, *Quart. Revs.*, 16 (1962) 208.
482. P. SCHOLLKOPF, *Angew. Chem.*, 71 (1959) 260.

SUBJECT INDEX

1. *This index should be used in conjunction with the table of contents at the beginning of the book.*
2. *Names of substances are not indexed unless the text contains more than a passing reference to them.*
3. *Words too generally used to be sufficiently indicative, such as olefin elimination and carbanion, are not indexed.*
4. *Where continuous reference to a subject extends over several pages, or where considerable discussion occurs, the entry is in italics.*

PRINTED IN THE NETHERLANDS

BY DRUKKERIJ MEIJER N.V. / WORMERVEER AND AMSTERDAM